HAMPTON-BROWN
HIGH POINT
SUCCESS IN LANGUAGE • LITERATURE • CONTENT

Reading Practice Book
The Basics

HAMPTON-BROWN

Hampton-Brown
P.O. Box 223220
Carmel, California 93922
1-800-333-3510

Printed in the United States of America
ISBN 0-7362-1225-6

06 07 08 09 10 11 16 15 14 13 12 11

Contents: Reading Practice Book for Lakeside School

Reading Practice Book Contents

© Hampton-Brown

Lakeside School

Word Work

Read each word. Then write it.

1. am _____
2. I _____
3. is _____
4. school _____
5. the _____
6. this _____
7. you _____

How to Play

1. Make a spinner.

2. Write the name of each player on a blank.

3. Spin. **Read the sentence.**

The first player to read all six sentences wins.

This is the ____.

This is the ____.

I am _____ .

I am _____ .

This is the ____.

This is the school.

Word Work

Read each word. Then write it.

1. a _____   4. my _____

2. an _____   5. no _____

3. here _____   6. yes _____

---

1. Find the words. Circle them.

Look across. ➡

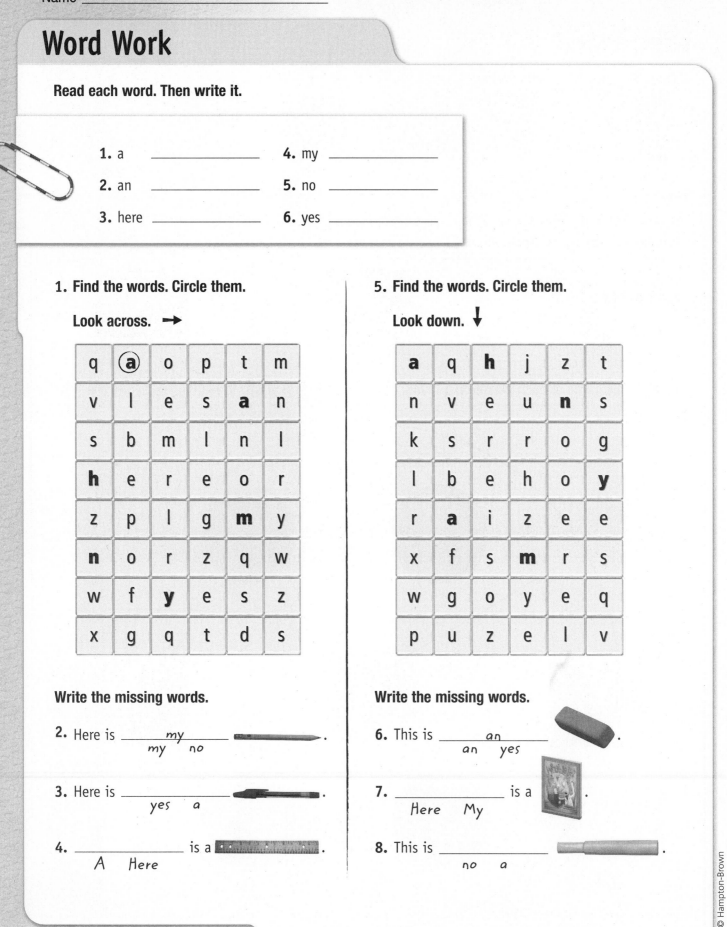

q	ⓐ	o	p	t	m
v	l	e	s	**a**	n
s	b	m	l	n	l
h	e	r	e	o	r
z	p	l	g	**m**	y
n	o	r	z	q	w
w	f	**y**	e	s	z
x	g	q	t	d	s

Write the missing words.

2. Here is _____*my*_____ 🖍.
         my   no

3. Here is _____ 🖊.
         yes   a

4. _____ is a 📏.
    A   Here

5. Find the words. Circle them.

Look down. ↓

a	q	**h**	j	z	t
n	v	e	u	**n**	s
k	s	r	r	o	g
l	b	e	h	o	**y**
r	**a**	i	z	e	e
x	f	s	**m**	r	s
w	g	o	y	e	q
p	u	z	e	l	v

Write the missing words.

6. This is _____*an*_____ .
         an   yes

7. _____ is a 📘.
    Here   My

8. This is _____ .
         no   a

Letters and Sounds

Study the new letters and sounds.

Ss   Mm   Ff   Hh   Tt   Aa

Say the name of each picture below. What letter spells the <u>first</u> sound you hear? Circle the letter.

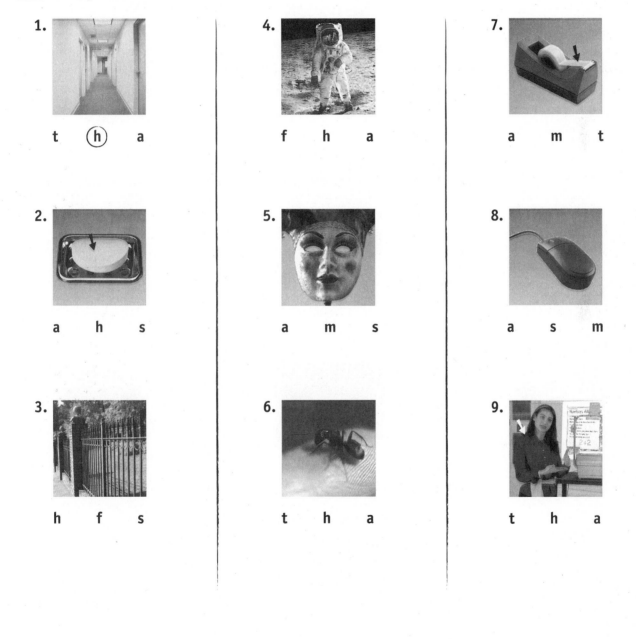

1.   t   (h)   a

2.   a   h   s

3.   h   f   s

4.   f   h   a

5.   a   m   s

6.   t   h   a

7.   a   m   t

8.   a   s   m

9.   t   h   a

Letters and Sounds

Say the name of each picture below. What letter spells the **first** sound you hear? Write the letter.

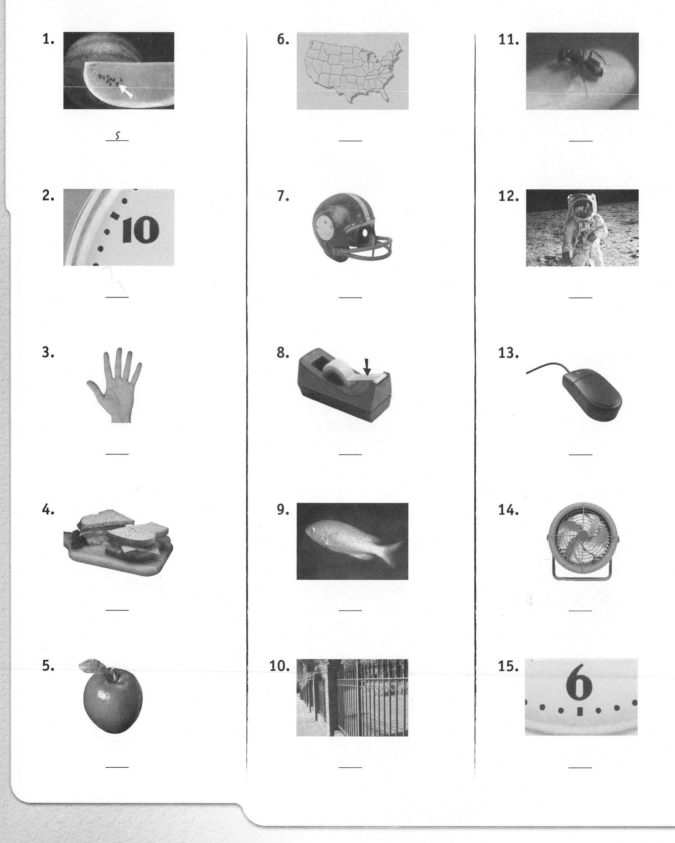

1. ___s___

2. _____

3. _____

4. _____

5. _____

6. _____

7. _____

8. _____

9. _____

10. _____

11. _____

12. _____

13. _____

14. _____

15. _____

Word Work

Read each word. Then write it.

1. at _____
2. it _____
3. look _____
4. of _____

5. on _____
6. see _____
7. show _____
8. where _____

Write the missing letters.

9. **Which words have a t?**

   _a_ _t_   ___ ___

10. **Which words have 2 letters?**

    ___ ___   ___ ___

    ___ ___   ___ ___

11. **Which word has 3 letters?**

    ___ ___ ___

12. **Which words have 4 letters?**

    ___ ___ ___ ___

    ___ ___ ___ ___

13. **Which word has 5 letters?**

    ___ ___ ___ ___ ___

14. **Which words start with o?**

    ___ ___   ___ ___

15. **Which word has an f?**

    ___ ___

Write the missing words.

16. I _____*see*_____ you.
         see   *where*

17. Carlos, _____ at this!
         show   *look*

18. Is this the school?

    Yes, _____ is.
         it   *at*

19. _____ me the school.
       Show   *Where*

20. _____ is the ☐ ?
       Look   *Where*

21. I am _____ school.
         at   *of*

22. This is a ☐ _____
             of   *show*

    the school.

23. The ☐ is _____ the ☐ .
           it   *on*

Words with Short *a*

Read each word. Draw a line to match the word and the picture.

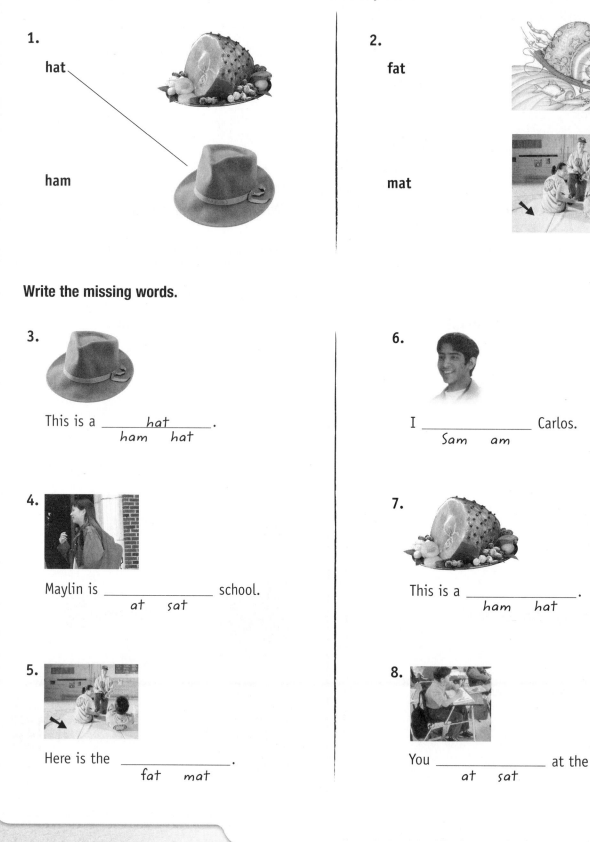

1.

hat

ham

2.

fat

mat

Write the missing words.

3.

This is a ___*hat*___ .
ham   hat

6.

I _____ Carlos.
Sam   am

4.

Maylin is _____ school.
at   sat

7.

This is a _____ .
ham   hat

5.

Here is the _____ .
fat   mat

8.

You _____ at the ___ .
at   sat

Words with Short *a*

Write the missing *a*. Then read the words in each list.
How are the words different?

1. _a_ m   2. ___ t   3. ___ t

    S ___ m   h ___ t   f ___ t

    h ___ m   s ___ t   m ___ t

What word completes each sentence and tells about the picture? Spell the word.

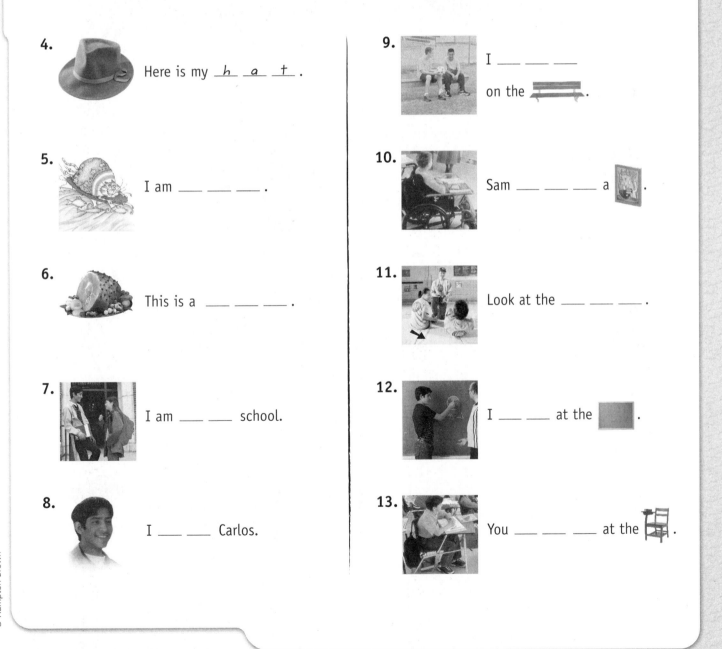

4. Here is my _h_ _a_ _t_ .

5. I am ___ ___ ___ .

6. This is a ___ ___ ___ .

7. I am ___ ___ school.

8. I ___ ___ Carlos.

9. I ___ ___ ___ on the _____ .

10. Sam ___ ___ ___ a ___ .

11. Look at the ___ ___ ___ .

12. I ___ ___ at the ___ .

13. You ___ ___ ___ at the ___ .

Word Work

Read each word. Then write it.

1. are _____
2. good _____
3. he _____
4. she _____

5. some _____
6. time _____
7. who _____
8. your _____

Write the missing letters.

9. **Which words have 4 letters?**

g o o d _ _ _ _

_ _ _ _   _ _ _ _

10. **Which word has an a?**

_ _ _

11. **Which word has 2 letters?**

_ _

12. **Which words have 3 letters?**

_ _ _

_ _ _

_ _ _

13. **Which word has a g?**

_ _ _ _

14. **Which word has a t?**

_ _ _ _

Write the missing word.

15. Here _____are_____ two \\ .
         are   your

16. What _____ is it?
      some   time

17. Where is _____?
      are   she

18. _____ is he?
    Good   Who

19. Is this _____?
    who   your

20. Here are _____ .
    time   some

21. _____ is Carlos.
    Some   He

22. This is a _____ .
    good   are

23. Here is _____ hat.
    who   your

Letters and Sounds

Study the new letters and sounds.

Nn　　Ll　　Pp　　Gg　　Ii

Say the name of each picture below. What letter spells the <u>first</u> sound you hear? Circle the letter.

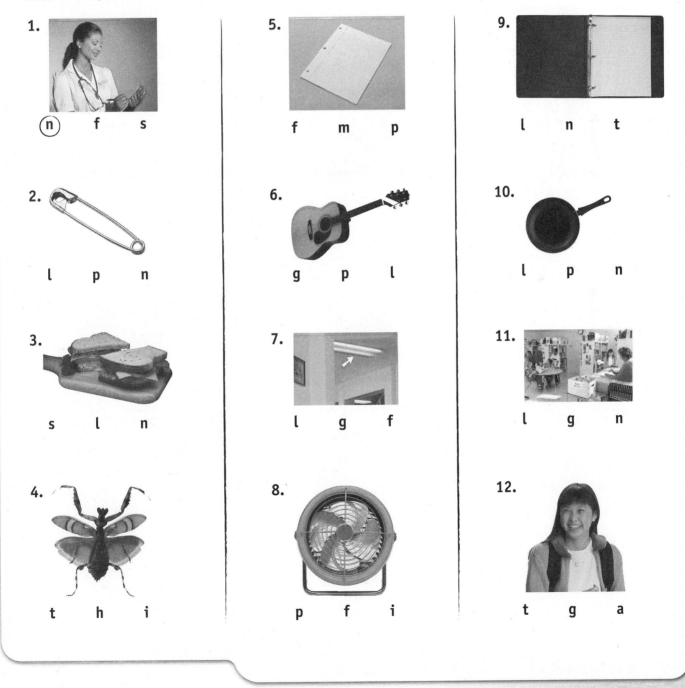

1. (n)　f　s

2. l　p　n

3. s　l　n

4. t　h　i

5. f　m　p

6. g　p　l

7. l　g　f

8. p　f　i

9. l　n　t

10. l　p　n

11. l　g　n

12. t　g　a

Letters and Sounds

Say the name of each picture below.
Write the missing letters.

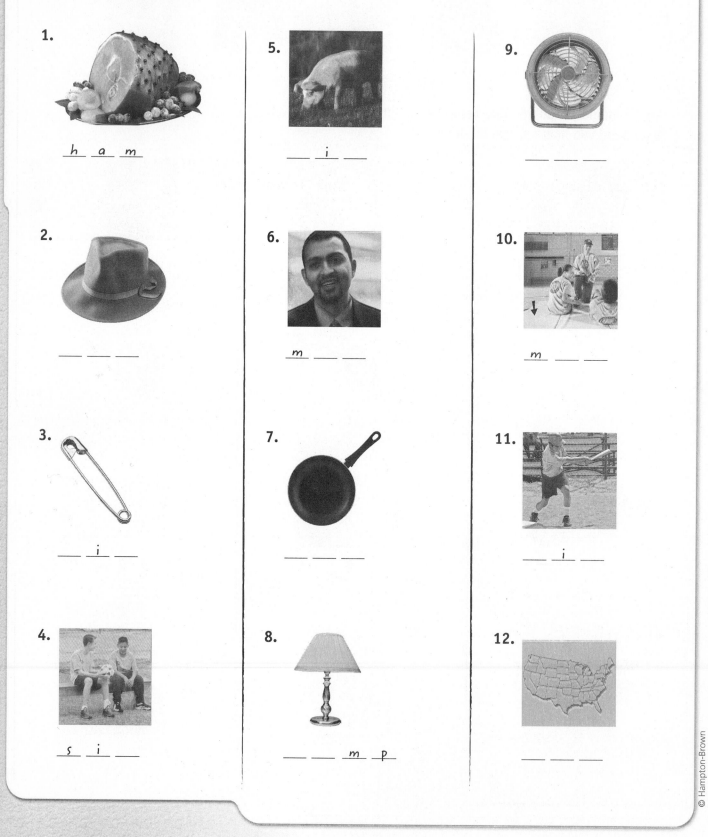

1. <u>h</u>   <u>a</u>   <u>m</u>

2. ___   ___   ___

3. ___   <u>i</u>   ___

4. <u>s</u>   <u>i</u>   ___

5. ___   <u>i</u>   ___

6. <u>m</u>   ___   ___

7. ___   ___   ___

8. ___   ___   <u>m</u>   <u>p</u>

9. ___   ___   ___

10. <u>m</u>   ___   ___

11. ___   <u>i</u>   ___

12. ___   ___   ___

Word Work

Read each word. Then write it.

1. answer _____
2. point _____
3. read _____
4. to _____

5. with _____
6. work _____
7. write _____

Write the missing words.

8. **Which word has 6 letters?**

  <u>a</u> <u>n</u> <u>s</u> <u>w</u> <u>e</u> <u>r</u>

9. **Which words have an <u>n</u>?**

  __ __ __ __ __ __

  __ __ __ __ __

10. **Which words have 5 letters?**

  __ __ __ __ __

  __ __ __ __ __

11. **Which words have 4 letters?**

  __ __ __ __

  __ __ __ __

  __ __ __ __

12. **Which word has a <u>p</u>?**

  __ __ __ __ __

13. **Which word has 2 letters?**

  __ __

Write the missing words.

14. Point ____<u>to</u>____ the ____ .
  with   to

15. I _____ the ____ .
  to   read

16. I show my _____ .
  work   with

17. I write the _____ .
  answer   read

18. _____ to the answer.
  With   Point

19. I work _____ you.
  to   with

20. _____ on the ____ .
  Write   To

21. Is this your _____ ?
  with   answer

22. _____ with a ____ .
  Write   To

Words with Short *a* and *i*

Read each word. Draw a line to match the word and the picture.

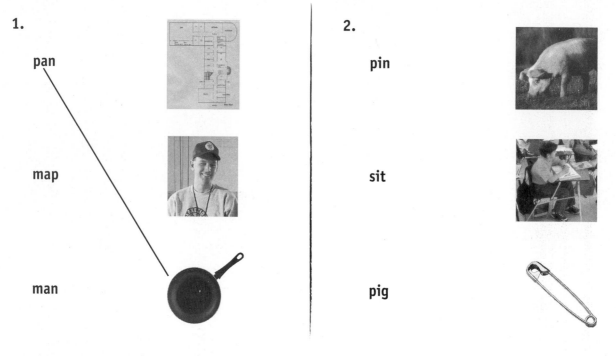

1.

pan

map

man

2.

pin

sit

pig

Write the missing words.

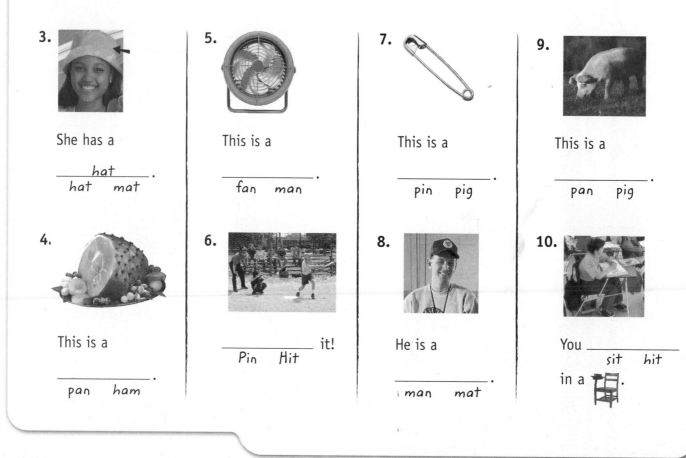

3. She has a

___hat___.
hat   mat

4. This is a

_____.
pan   ham

5. This is a

_____.
fan   man

6. _____ it!
Pin   Hit

7. This is a

_____.
pin   pig

8. He is a

_____.
man   mat

9. This is a

_____.
pan   pig

10. You _____
sit   hit
in a 🪑.

Words with Short *a* and *i*

Write the missing letters. Then read the words in each list.
How are the words different?

1. h _ _

 _ _ _

 _ _ _

2. p _ _

_ _ _

 _ _ _

Read each question. What word goes in the answer? Spell the word.
Then circle the correct picture.

3. Where is the pig?

The _p_ _i_ _g_ is here.

4. Where is the pan?

Here is the _ _ _.

5. Where is Sam? _ _ _ is here.

6. Who hit it?

Carlos _ _ _ it.

7. Who has the hat?

She _ _ _ the hat.

8. Who is the man? He is a _ _ _.

Word Work

Read each word. Then write it.

1. call _____
2. name _____
3. need _____

4. number _____
5. to _____
6. what _____

Write the missing letters.

7. Which word has 2 letters?

   _t_ _o_

8. Which words have 4 letters?

   — — — —

   — — — —

   — — — —

   — — — —

9. Which word has 6 letters.

   — — — — — —

10. Which words have a <u>t</u>?

    — —

    — — — —

11. Which words have an <u>n</u>?

    — — — —

    — — — —

    — — — — — —

12. Which word has an <u>l</u> at the end?

    — — — —

Write the missing word.

13. My _____name_____ is Ana.
    number   name

14. I _____ to show my work.
    what   need

15. My phone _____ is 678-5335.
    number   name

16. I can _____ Carlos.
    call   what

17. _____ is your name?
    What   Need

18. I need _____ see you.
    name   to

Circle each number.

19. m   f   85   p   g

     19   i   20   a   n

     s   50   h   t   7

Letters and Sounds

Study the new letters and sounds.

Rr   **Dd**   **Cc**   **Vv**   **Oo**

Say the name of each picture below. What letter spells the
first sound you hear? Circle the letter.

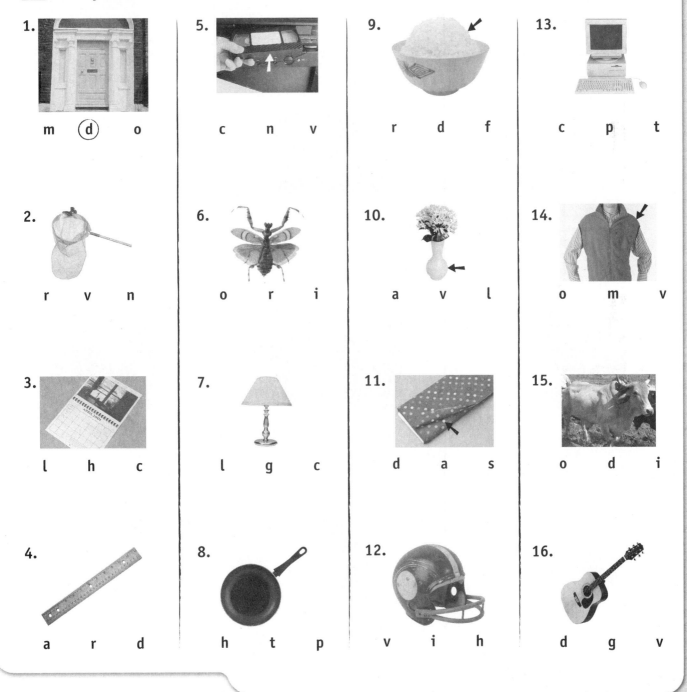

1.   m   (d)   o

2.   r   v   n

3.   l   h   c

4.   a   r   d

5.   c   n   v

6.   o   r   i

7.   l   g   c

8.   h   t   p

9.   r   d   f

10.   a   v   l

11.   d   a   s

12.   v   i   h

13.   c   p   t

14.   o   m   v

15.   o   d   i

16.   d   g   v

Letters and Sounds

Say the name of each picture below.
Write the missing letters.

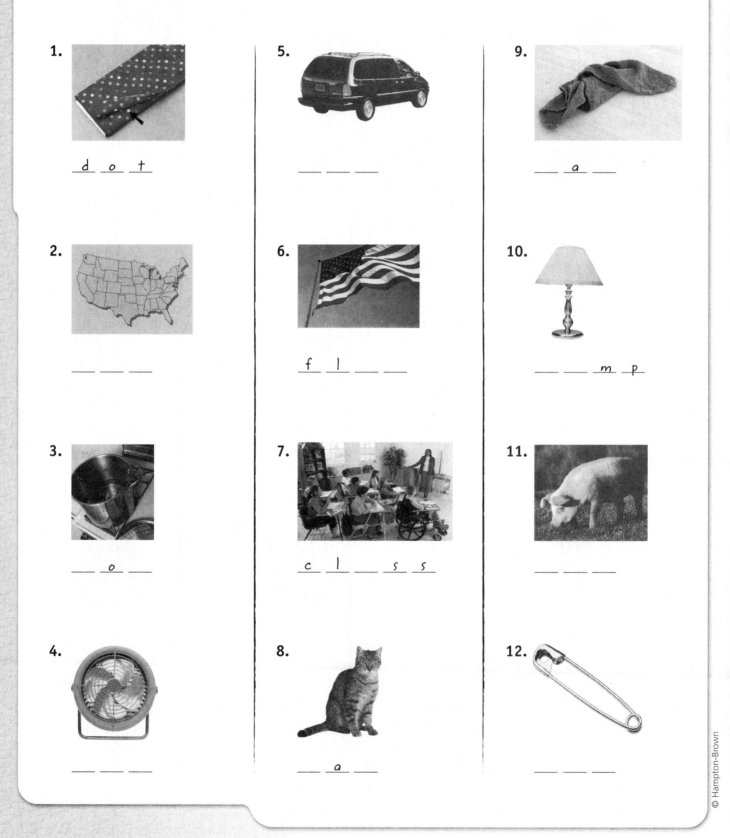

1. d o t

2. ___ ___ ___

3. ___ o ___

4. ___ ___ ___

5. ___ ___ ___

6. f l ___ ___

7. c l ___ s s

8. ___ a ___

9. ___ a ___

10. ___ ___ m p

11. ___ ___ ___

12. ___ ___ ___

Word Work

Read each word. Then write it.

1. do _____	**6.** like _____
2. does _____	**7.** me _____
3. for _____	**8.** picture _____
4. help _____	**9.** will _____
5. in _____	

How to Play

1. Play with a partner.   **1** **2**   Each partner chooses a sign. X O

2. Partner 1 reads a word and marks the square with a sign. **1**

3. Then Partner 2 takes a turn. **2**

4. Get 3 Xs or Os in a row to win.

A.

do	help	like
in	does	will
me	picture	for

B.

picture	like	in
does	me	for
will	do	help

C.

help	does	me
do	will	for
like	in	picture

D.

does	will	help
picture	me	in
for	like	do

Words with Short *a*, *i*, and *o*

Read each word. Draw a line to the correct picture.

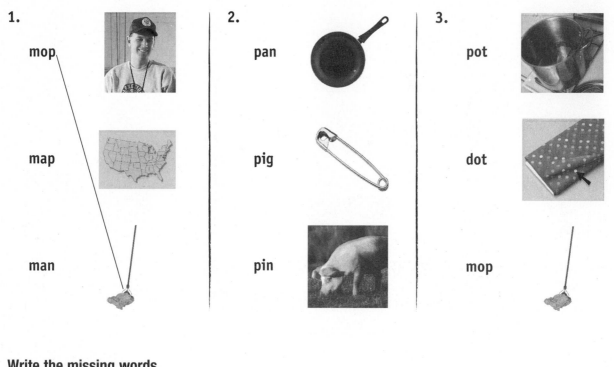

1.
mop
map
man

2.
pan
pig
pin

3.
pot
dot
mop

Write the missing words.

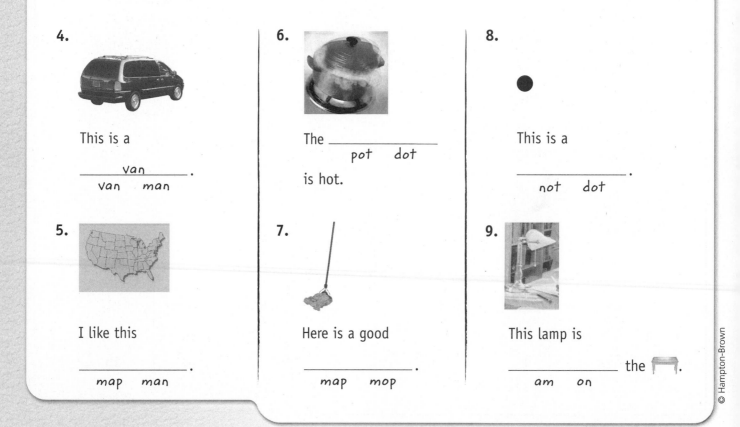

4.
This is a

___van___.
van   man

5.
I like this

_____.
map   man

6.
The _____
pot   dot
is hot.

7.
Here is a good

_____.
map   mop

8.
This is a

_____.
not   dot

9.
This lamp is

_____ the ▭.
am   on

Words with Short *a*, *i*, and *o*

**Write the missing letters. Then read the words in each list.
How are the words different?**

1.
___c___ ___ ___

___ ___ ___

___ ___ ___

2.
___p___ ___ ___

___ ___ ___

___ ___ ___

3.
___h___ ___ ___

___ ___ ___

___ ___ ___

Read each question and the answer. Write the missing words. Then circle the correct picture.

4. Is this pot hot?

No, the __p__ __o__ __t__ is __n__ __o__ __t__ hot.

5. Is this your cap?

Yes, it is my ___ ___ ___ .

6. Where is the mop?

The ___ ___ ___ is here.

7. Where can I sit?

You can ___ ___ ___ here.

8. Point to the dot.

The ___ ___ ___ is here!

✔   ●

9. Do you like the hat?

Yes, I like the ___ ___ ___ .

Word Work

Read each word. Then write it.

1. around _____   4. too _____

2. can _____   5. we _____

3. play _____

Write the missing letters.

6. **Which words have 3 letters?**

   <u>c</u> <u>a</u> <u>n</u>

   ___ ___ ___

7. **Which word has 6 letters?**

   ___ ___ ___ ___ ___ ___

8. **Which word has 4 letters?**

   ___ ___ ___ ___

9. **Which word has an <u>r</u>?**

   ___ ___ ___ ___ ___ ___

10. **Which word that has 2 letters?**

    ___ ___

11. **Which word has a <u>t</u>?**

    ___ ___ ___

12. **Which word has a <u>d</u>?**

    ___ ___ ___ ___ ___ ___

13. **Which words have an <u>n</u>?**

    ___ ___ ___ ___ ___

    ___ ___ ___

Write the missing word.

14. Can you ____<u>play</u>____ 🏀 ?
    $\qquad$ play   we

15. Yes, I _____ play 🏀 .
    $\qquad$ around   can

16. Dan and I play, _____!
    $\qquad$ too   can

17. _____ play at school.
    $\qquad$ Too   We

18. Can you _____ the ?
    $\qquad$ around   we

19. Yes, we _____!
    $\qquad$ can   around

20. I can, _____.
    $\qquad$ we   too

21. Can you _____ ?
    $\qquad$ around   play

22. Yes, _____ can.
    $\qquad$ too   we

Letters and Sounds

Study the new letters and sounds.

Jj   Bb   Ww   Kk   Ee

How to Play Bingo

1. Write the letters from the box.

2. Then listen to the word your teacher reads.

3. Put a ◯ on the letter that stands for the first sound in the word.

4. The first player to cover all the letters in a row is the winner.

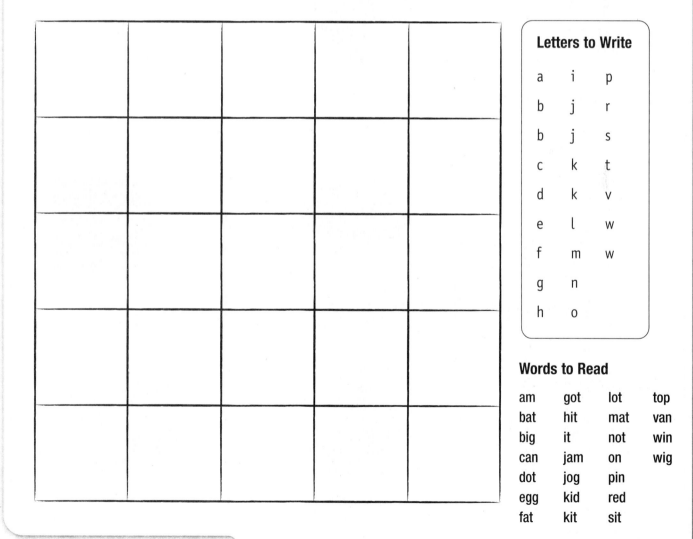

Letters to Write

a	i	p
b	j	r
b	j	s
c	k	t
d	k	v
e	l	w
f	m	w
g	n	
h	o	

Words to Read

am	got	lot	top
bat	hit	mat	van
big	it	not	win
can	jam	on	wig
dot	jog	pin	
egg	kid	red	
fat	kit	sit	

Letters and Sounds

Say the name of each picture below.
Write the missing letters.

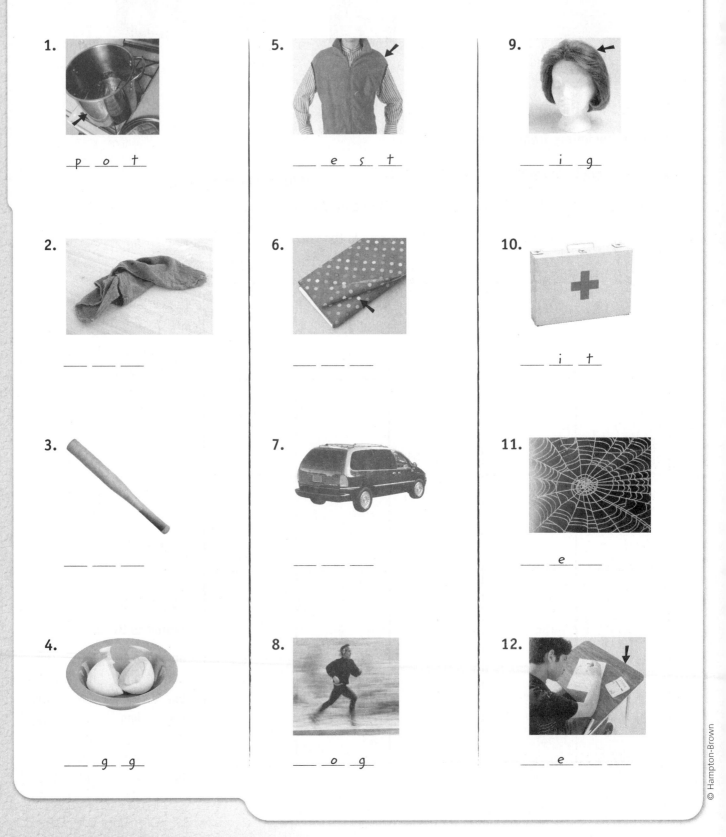

1. __p__ __o__ __t__

2. ___ ___ ___

3. ___ ___ ___

4. ___ __g__ __g__

5. ___ __e__ __s__ __t__

6. ___ ___ ___

7. ___ ___ ___

8. ___ __o__ __g__

9. ___ __i__ __g__

10. ___ __i__ __t__

11. ___ __e__ ___

12. ___ __e__ ___

Word Work

Read each word. Then write it.

1. feel _____
2. has _____
3. have _____

4. how _____
5. put _____
6. they _____

Write the missing letters.

7. Which words start with <u>h</u>?

 h a s   __ __ __

 __ __ __ __

8. Which word has a <u>p</u>?

 __ __ __

9. Which words have 3 letters?

 __ __ __ __   __ __ __

 __ __ __ __

10. Which words have 4 letters?

 __ __ __ __   __ __ __ __

 __ __ __ __

11. Which word has an <u>f</u>?

 __ __ __ __

12. Which word has a <u>v</u>?

 __ __ __ __

13. Which word has an <u>l</u>?

 __ __ __ __

14. Which word has an <u>s</u>?

 __ __ __

Write the missing word.

15. _____How_____ do you feel?
     Put   How

16. I _____ good.
      feel   put

17. I _____ bad.
      feel   has

18. _____ feel bad.
     They   Have

19. Do you _____ a ⊞ ?
      have   they

20. She _____ a kit.
      how   has

21. _____ the kit here.
      How   Put

Words with Short *a*, *i*, *o*, and *e*

Read each word. Draw a line to the correct picture.

1.

jam

ham

hat

2.

pen

ten

men

3.

cat

bat

bed

Write the missing words.

4.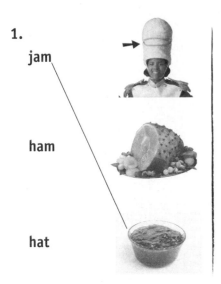

Here are two

___men___.

men   ten

5. ● ● ● ● ●
   ● ● ● ● ●

There are

_____ dots.

ten   pen

6.

My pet is a

_____.

pig   pin

7.

This is a good

_____.

pan   pen

8.

He can _____

hot   hit

the ◯.

9.

This is my

_____.

cap   map

10.

Here is a

_____.

bed   Ed

11.

I do _____

dot   not

like to play.

12.

Put it in the

_____.

pot   pat

Words with Short *a*, *i*, *o*, and *e*

**Write the missing letters. Then read the words in each list.
How are the words different?**

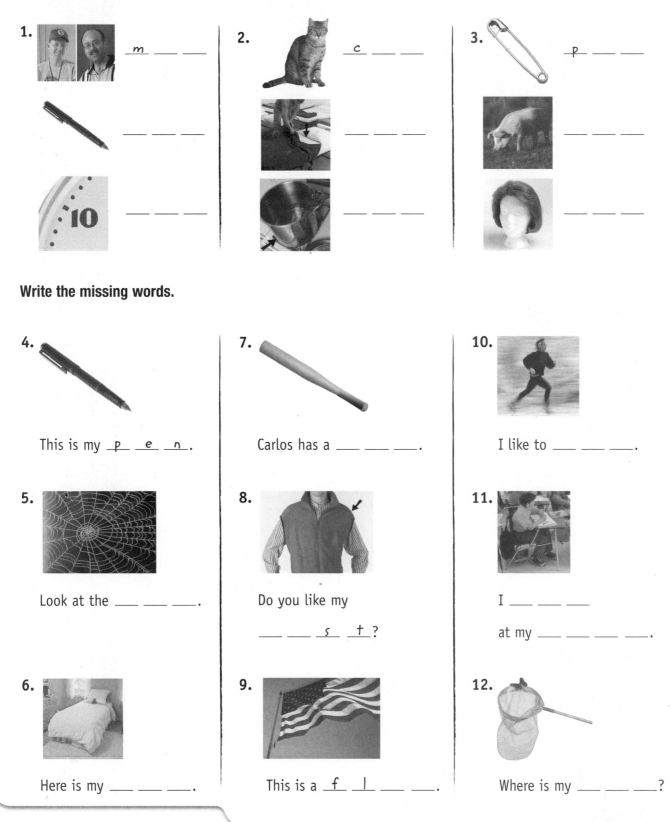

1. _m_ __ __

   __ __ __

   __ __ __

2. _c_ __ __

   __ __ __

   __ __ __

3. _p_ __ __

   __ __ __

   __ __ __

Write the missing words.

4. This is my _p_ _e_ _n_ .

5. Look at the __ __ __ .

6. Here is my __ __ __ .

7. Carlos has a __ __ __ .

8. Do you like my
__ __ _s_ _t_ ?

9. This is a _f_ _l_ __ __ .

10. I like to __ __ __ .

11. I __ __ __
at my __ __ __ __ .

12. Where is my __ __ __ ?

Word Work

Read each word. Then write it.

1. and _____
2. don't _____
3. food _____
4. not _____
5. that _____

Write the missing letters.

6. **Which words have 3 letters?**

   _a_ _n_ _d_

   ___ ___ ___

7. **Which words have an a?**

   ___ ___

   ___ ___ ___ ___

8. **Which word has an f?**

   ___ ___ ___ ___

9. **Which words have an n?**

   ___ ___ ___

   ___ ___ ___ ' ___

   ___ ___ ___

10. **Which words end in a t?**

    ___ ___ ___ ' ___

    ___ ___ ___

    ___ ___ ___ ___

Write the missing word.

11. I like ___that___ food.
    and   that

12. I do _____ like that food.
    and   not

13. I like the _____ .
    and   food

14. I _____ like .
    that   don't

15. This _____ is good for you.
    and   food

16. Is this food?

    No, it is _____ food.
    and   not

17. This is _____ a .
    and   don't

18. What is _____ ?
    not   that

19. This _____ is good.
    and   food

How to Write a Statement

A **statement** tells something.

It starts with a capital letter.

It ends with a period.

Examples: This is Lakeside School.

There are many students here.

Read each statement. Is it written correctly? If so, put a ✓ next to it. If not, correct it.

1. ✓ We are at school.

2. ☐ It is time for lunch.

3. ☐ She is in the cafeteria

4. ☐ He has some pizza.

5. ☐ you can have some food.

6. ☐ this is a salad

7. ☐ This is a sandwich.

8. ☐ Now it is time for class.

Write each statement correctly.

9. Ron is here

    Ron is here.

10. Kim is here, too

_____

11. here is the food

_____

12. I like the taco and beans

_____

13. my friends don't like bagels

_____

14. I have a cookie

_____

15. we have some milk

_____

16. the food is good

_____

Word Work

Read each word. Then write it.

1. give _____   3. think _____

2. take _____

How to Play

1. **Get 25 paper clips.**   **Play with a partner.**

2. **Use an eraser or other small object as your game piece.**
   Use a coin to show how many spaces to move.

   Heads = 1 space   Tails = 2 spaces

3. **Read the sentence. Then do what it says.**
   The player with more paper clips at the end wins.

FINISH

Give 1 paper clip.

Take 5 paper clips.

Take 2 paper clips.

Give 7 paper clips.

START

Take 1 paper clip.

Give 2 paper clips.

Give 3 paper clips.

Give 5 paper clips.

Take 4 paper clips.

Take 1 paper clip.

Give 3 paper clips.

Take 6 paper clips.

Letters and Sounds

Study the new letters and sounds.

| Zz | Yy | Uu | Qq | Xx |

How to Play Bingo

1. Write the letters from the box.

2. Then listen to the word your teacher reads.

3. Put a ⬭ on the letter that stands for the first sound in the word.

4. The first player to cover all the letters in a row is the winner.

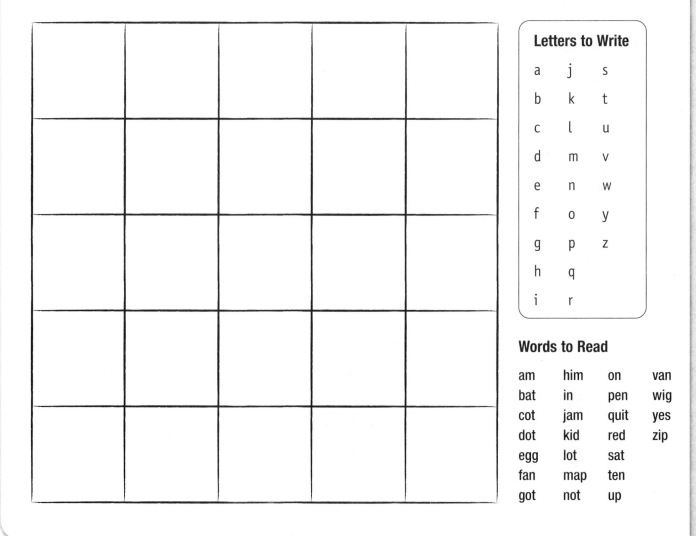

Letters to Write

a	j	s
b	k	t
c	l	u
d	m	v
e	n	w
f	o	y
g	p	z
h	q	
i	r	

Words to Read

am	him	on	van
bat	in	pen	wig
cot	jam	quit	yes
dot	kid	red	zip
egg	lot	sat	
fan	map	ten	
got	not	up	

Letters and Sounds

Say the name of each picture below.
Write the missing letters.

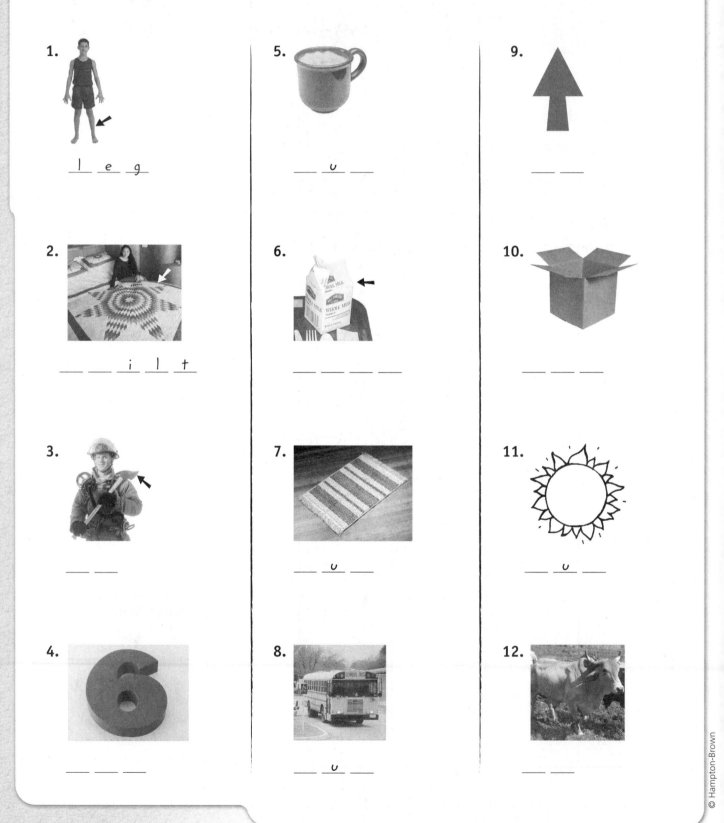

1. __l__ __e__ __g__

2. ___ ___ __i__ __l__ __t__

3. ___ ___

4. ___ ___ ___

5. ___ __u__ ___

6. ___ ___ ___ ___

7. ___ __u__ ___

8. ___ __u__ ___

9. ___ ___

10. ___ ___ ___

11. ___ __u__ ___

12. ___ ___ ___

Word Work

Read each word. Then write it.

1. both _____
2. get _____
3. little _____
4. old _____
5. them _____

6. these _____
7. things _____
8. those _____
9. very _____
10. which _____

Read the sentence. Write the missing word on the blank and in the crossword puzzle.

DOWN ↓

1. I like ___*both*___ the shorts and the T-shirt.

3. Which _____ do you like?

5. I like _____ blue shorts that I have.

6. My pants are _____.
   I need new ones.

8. I like the pants and the shorts.
   I like both of _____.

ACROSS →

2. Carlos will _____ a T-shirt.

4. Carlos, _____ caps do you like?

5. I like _____ green caps on the table.

7. I like the _____ T-shirt on the lion!

9. My T-shirt is not _____ old.

Words with Short *a*, *i*, *o*, *e*, and *u*

Read each word. Draw a line to the correct picture.

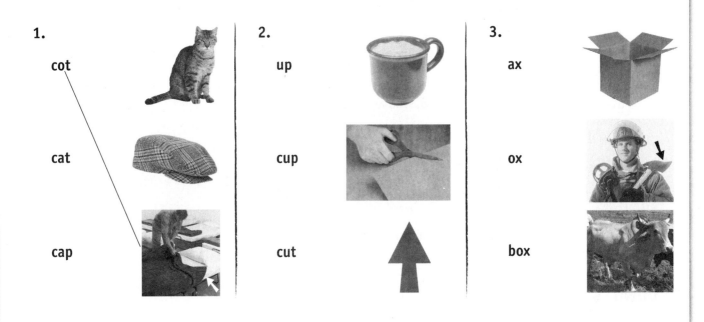

1.

cot

cat

cap

2.

up

cup

cut

3.

ax

ox

box

Write the missing words.

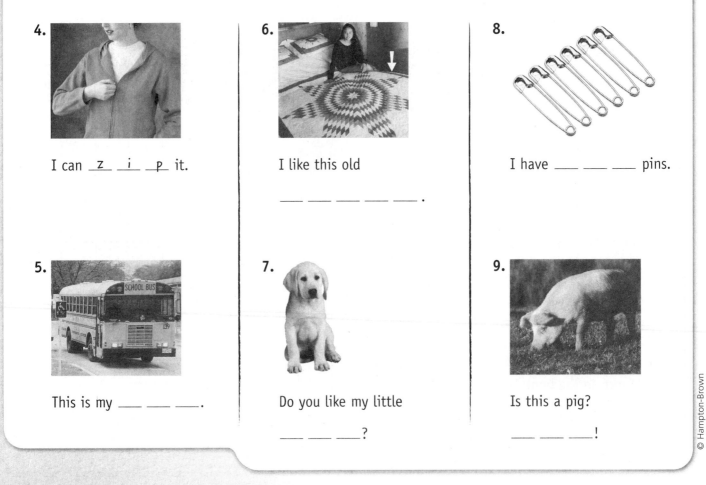

4.

I can _z_ _i_ _p_ it.

6.

I like this old
___ ___ ___ ___ .

8.

I have ___ ___ ___ pins.

5.

This is my ___ ___ ___.

7.

Do you like my little
___ ___ ___?

9.

Is this a pig?
___ ___ ___!

Words with Short *a, i, o, e,* and *u*

Write the missing letters. Then read the words in each list.
How are the words different?

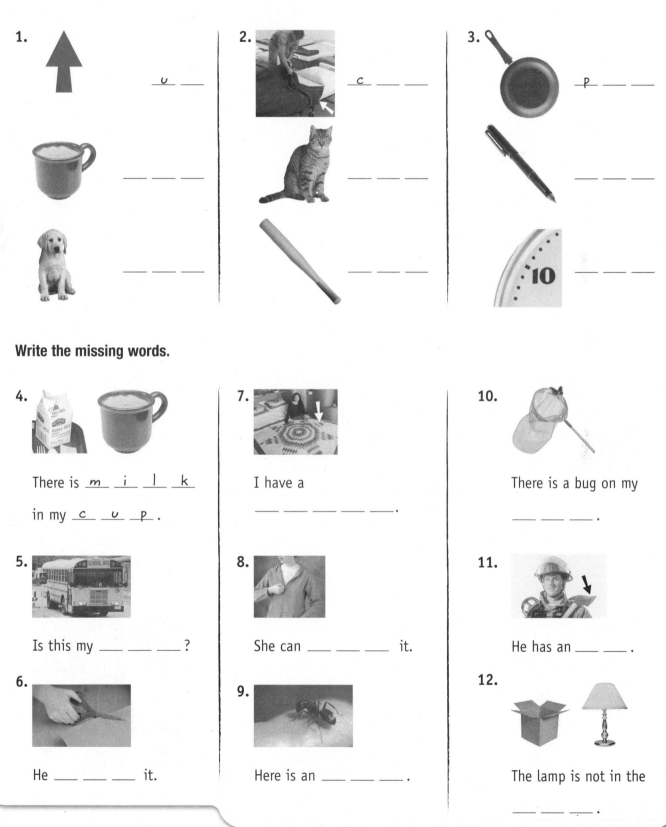

1.
_u_ _ _

_ _ _

_ _ _

2.
_c_ _ _

_ _ _

_ _ _

3.
_p_ _ _

_ _ _

_ _ _

Write the missing words.

4.
There is _m_ _i_ _l_ _k_
in my _c_ _u_ _p_ .

5.
Is this my _ _ _ ?

6.
He _ _ _ it.

7.
I have a
_ _ _ _ .

8.
She can _ _ _ it.

9.
Here is an _ _ _ .

10.
There is a bug on my
_ _ _ .

11.
He has an _ _ .

12.
The lamp is not in the
_ _ _ .

Word Work

Read each word. Then write it.

1. great _____   3. soon _____

2. later _____   4. tomorrow _____

Write the missing word in each sentence.

5. I need your work _____tomorrow_____ .
$\qquad$ great   tomorrow

6. That is too _____ ! I think I need help!
$\qquad$ soon   later

7. I can help you _____ at 4:00.
$\qquad$ great   later

8. _____ !
$\qquad$ Great   Soon

9. See you _____ .
$\qquad$ later   great

10. See you _____ !
$\qquad$ great   soon

Work with 2 partners.

Act out the story.

Read the sentences with your group.

How to Write a Question

A **question** asks something.

It starts with a capital letter.

It ends with a question mark.

Examples: Is this your school?

Are Carlos and Maylin here?

Read each question. Is it written correctly? If so, put a ✓ next to it. If not, correct it.

1. ✓ Is the basketball game on Tuesday?

2. ☐ what is your number

3. ☐ Are they here

4. ☐ Can he play on Wednesday?

5. ☐ do you like basketball?

6. ☐ Will you call me later?

7. ☐ Does Carlos want to play on Sunday

8. ☐ Who is with Maylin?

Write each question correctly.

9. is this the basketball court

   Is this the basketball court?
   _____

10. where are my friends

   _____

11. is it 4:00

   _____

12. do you like basketball

   _____

13. can you play on Tuesday

   _____

14. does carlos like basketball

   _____

15. which basketball do you need

   _____

16. can we get the basketball on Friday

   _____

Word Work

Read each word. Then write it.

1. book _____
2. boy _____
3. day _____
4. girl _____

5. group _____
6. letters _____
7. night _____
8. year _____

Write the missing letters.

9. **Which words have an l?**

   g   i   r   l

   __ __ __ __ __ __

10. **Which words have 5 letters?**

    __ __ __ __ __

    __ __ __ __ __

11. **Which word has a p?**

    __ __ __ __ __

12. **Which words have a b?**

    __ __ __ __

    __ __ __

Write the name of each thing.

13.

December 6

November 13
Dear Grandma and Grandpa,
I really like it here at
Lakeside School. I have met
lots of new friends. I have
great teachers, too. My favorite
subject is math. I miss you.
                    Love,
                    Carlos

letters
_____
letters   day

14.

Good News

_____
girl   book

15.

_____
year   night

16.

_____
boy   girl

17.

_____
girl   book

18.

_____
night   group

© Hampton-Brown

How to Write an Exclamation

An **exclamation** shows a strong feeling.

It starts with a <u>capital letter</u>.

It ends with an <u>exclamation mark</u>.

Examples: <u>H</u>elp me<u>!</u>

<u>L</u>ook at that<u>!</u>

Read each exclamation. Is it written correctly? If so, put a ✔ next to it. If not, correct it.

1. ✔ See you soon!

2. ☐ listen

3. ☐ Here they are

4. ☐ This is good work!

5. ☐ I like that food

6. ☐ call me tomorrow

7. ☐ Carlos is here

8. ☐ great!

Write each exclamation correctly.

9. we can do that in October

   <u>We can do that in October!</u>

10. this book is great

   _____

11. see you later

   _____

12. Carlos likes this one

   _____

13. this is great work

   _____

14. call me on Friday

   _____

15. he looks great

   _____

16. June will be fun

   _____

Units 1-18

Words to Know

READ AND WRITE

Read each word. Then write it.

1. new _____   2. many _____   3. one _____

4. from _____   5. first _____   6. then _____

7. go _____   8. next _____   9. there _____

10. home _____

WORD WORK

Read each sentence. Find the new words in the box.
Write the words on the lines.

11. These 2 words have 3 letters.

    ___new___   ___one___

12. These 2 words begin with **th**.

    _____   _____

13. These 3 words have an **m**.

    _____   _____

    _____

14. This word rhymes with **where**.

    _____

15. This word is the opposite of **stop**.

    _____

16. These 4 words have an **o**.

    _____   _____

    _____   _____

17. These 3 words tell "when."

    _____   _____

    _____

18. These 5 words have 4 letters each.

    _____   _____

    _____   _____

    _____

SHORT A, SHORT O

Words with Short a and Short o

Name each picture. Write the name.

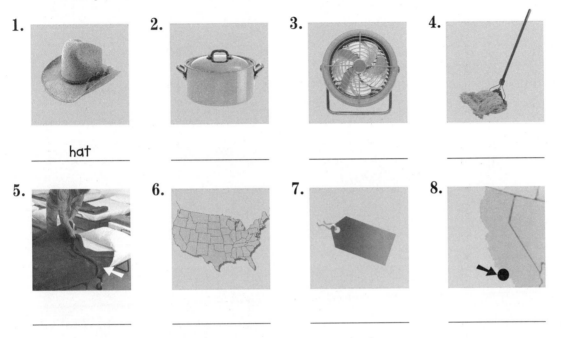

1. hat

2. _____

3. _____

4. _____

5. _____

6. _____

7. _____

8. _____

Now read the story. Circle the words with short a or short o.
Write them in the chart. Write each word one time.

I See a (Van)

I see a van.

It has a lot of things in it!

I see a map and a box in the van.

I see a mop and a fan in the van.

I see some pots and pans, too.

Is Tom in the van?

Tom is not in the van. There is no room!

9. van	15. _____
10. _____	16. _____
11. _____	17. _____
12. _____	18. _____
13. _____	19. _____
14. _____	20. _____

More Words with Short a and Short o

Read each word. Which picture goes with the word? Write its letter.

1. cot __G__ 2. cap __ 3. fan __ 4. top __ 5. jog __

6. bag __ 7. fog __ 8. dot __ 9. van __ 10. rag __

11. hop __ 12. bat __ 13. nap __ 14. hat __ 15. sad __

A. B. C. D. E.

F. G. H. I. J.

K. L. M. N. O.

Name each picture below. Which word or words above rhyme
with the picture name? Write the words on the lines.

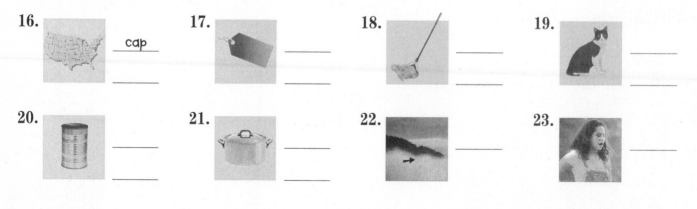

16. _cap_ ____ 17. ____ 18. ____ 19. ____

20. ____ 21. ____ 22. ____ 23. ____

COMPREHENSION

Build Reading Fluency

Some sentences tell something. Other sentences show strong feeling.

This sentence tells something.
It ends with a period.

> Lupe is new at Lakeside School**.**

This sentence shows a strong feeling.
It ends with an exclamation mark.

> Lupe is glad to have 2 new friends**!**

LISTEN AND LEARN TO READ

Listen to the different kinds of sentences.

New at School

Lupe is new at Lakeside School.
First she has science lab with Pat and Ron.
Pat helps Lupe.
Next they have P.E. class.
Pat and Lupe go fast. Ron does not go fast.
He has a cold and has to stop!
Then Pat, Lupe, and Ron go to lunch.
They have a lot of hot soup.
At last it is time to go home.
Lupe is glad to have 2 new friends!

PRACTICE

Now read the sentences above. Work with a partner.

Say each kind of sentence with the right expression.

See how your reading improves!

Words to Know

READ AND WRITE

Read each word. Then write it.

1. large _____	2. open _____	3. small _____
4. different _____	5. long _____	6. same _____
7. make _____	8. eat _____	9. move _____
10. something _____		

WORD WORK

Read the clue. Write the word in the chart.

Then write the word again in the sentence.

What to Look For	Word	Sentence
11. starts with **o**	o p e n	I _____open_____ my lunch.
12. starts with **sm**	_ _ _ _ _	It is in a _____ bag.
13. has **ff**	_ _ _ _ _ _ _ _ _	Your bag is _____.
14. means "big"	_ _ _ _ _	You have a _____ bag.
15. ends with **ve**	_ _ _ _	Please _____ over.
16. has 3 letters	_ _ _	It is time to _____.
17. has the word **some** in it	_ _ _ _ _ _ _ _ _	I want _____ hot.
18. rhymes with **song**	_ _ _ _	I like _____ noodles.
19. ends with **me**	_ _ _ _	Our food is not the _____.
20. rhymes with **take**	_ _ _ _	You _____ great food.

SHORT *I*, SHORT *U*

Words with Short i and Short u

Name each picture. Write the name.

1. _____pin_____

2. _____

3. _____

4. _____

5. _____

6. _____

7. _____

8. _____

Now read the story. Circle the words with short i or short u.
Write them in the chart. Write each word one time.

(Just) Great!

Sam needs something to eat.

He rips open a bag of chips.

The chips are good, but not great.

Sam cuts a bit of ham and
slaps it on a bun.

The ham is good, but not great.

Mom comes in.

She gets a cup of ice cream.

She adds lots of nuts.

Sam grins. Yes! That's great!

9. ___Just___	15. _____
10. _____	16. _____
11. _____	17. _____
12. _____	18. _____
13. _____	19. _____
14. _____	20. _____
	21. _____

More Words with Short i and Short u

Read each word. Which picture goes with the word? Write its letter.

1. cup <u>G</u>   **2.** fin ___   **3.** pump ___   **4.** hit ___   **5.** sit ___

6. rug ___   **7.** disk ___   **8.** nut ___   **9.** pig ___   **10.** dig ___

11. sun ___   **12.** pin ___   **13.** cut ___   **14.** lid ___   **15.** bun ___

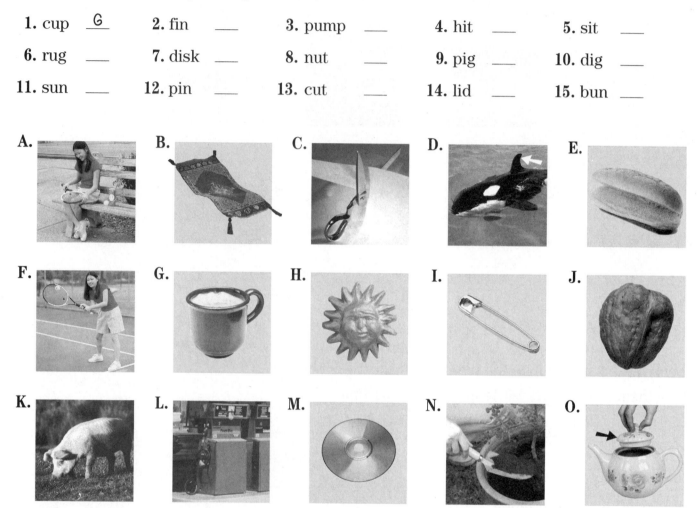

**Name each picture below. Which word or words above rhyme
with the picture name? Write the words on the lines.**

16. <u>bun</u>
___

17. ___

18. ___
___

19. ___

20. ___

21. ___
___

22. ___

Build Reading Fluency

When you read, pause between groups of words that go together.

Kim likes hot dogs / for lunch.

She cooks / a batch of hot dogs / in a big pot.

LISTEN AND LEARN TO READ

Listen to the story. Which groups of words does the reader say together?
Where does he pause? When you hear a pause, write a **/**.

Example: Kim likes hot dogs **/** for lunch.

Something Good for Lunch

Kim likes hot dogs for lunch.
She cooks a batch of hot dogs in a big pot.
Next Kim chops some small onions.
She opens a large bag of buns.
She fills the buns with hot dogs, mustard, and onions.
She opens a bag of chips, too.
She pours a cup of punch.
This is too much food to eat!
Kim calls Mitch.
Then they sit and eat a great lunch!

PRACTICE

Now read the story to a partner. Read groups of words together.
Pause when you see a **/**.

HIGH FREQUENCY WORDS

Words to Know

READ AND WRITE

Read each word. Then write it.

1. carry _____	2. face _____	3. say _____
4. learn _____	5. find _____	6. use _____
7. study _____	8. love _____	9. want _____
10. when _____		

Find each word in the box. Write it on the line.

11. This word has 2 **r**'s.

_____

12. This word means "like a lot."

_____

WORD WORK

Read each sentence. Find the new words in the box.
Write the words on the lines.

13. These 3 words have 5 letters each.

_____carry_____   _____learn_____

_____study_____

14. This word rhymes with **day**.

_____

15. This word has an **i**.

_____

16. This word starts with **st**.

_____

17. These 3 words end with **e**.

_____   _____

_____

18. This word ends with **nt**.

_____

19. This word rhymes with **then**.

_____

20. These 2 words start with **l**.

_____   _____

SHORT E AND CK

Words with Short e

Read each word. Which picture goes with the word? Write its letter.

1. hen F
2. check ___
3. net ___
4. pet ___

5. bed ___
6. chest ___
7. pen ___
8. vet ___

9. egg ___
10. bench ___
11. stretch ___
12. send ___

A. B. C. D.

E. F. G. H.

I. J. K. L.

Name each picture below. Which words above rhyme with
the picture name? Write the words on the lines.

13. ___pet___
_____
_____

14. _____
_____

CK AND DOUBLE CONSONANTS

Final ll, ss, zz, ck

Read each word. Which picture goes with the word? Write its letter.

1. chick _A_
2. pill ___
3. bell ___
4. fizz ___

5. check ___
6. jazz ___
7. kiss ___
8. spill ___

9. rock ___
10. sick ___
11. dress ___
12. hill ___

A.   B.   C.   D.

E.   F.   G.   H.

I.   J.   K.   L.

Name each picture below. What is the last sound? Find the words above that have the same sound at the end. Write the words on the lines.

13.   _____
_____
_____

14.   _____
_____
_____

Build Reading Fluency

Some sentences ask something. Other sentences show strong feeling.

This sentence asks a question.
It ends with a question mark.

> Do you want to send something **?**

This sentence shows a strong feeling.
It ends with an exclamation mark.

> Then he hops on his bike and … zip **!**

LISTEN AND LEARN TO READ

Listen to the reader's voice. Listen for sentences that ask
a question or show a strong feeling.

Let Ben Take It

Ben is a bike messenger.
Do you want to send something?
Ben can get it there fast.
Just tell him where it must go.
He gets his map.
He uses it to find a shop.
Then he hops on his bike and … zip!
He is off like a jet.
Ben can carry a lot of different things:
food, pictures, letters, flowers.
They fit in the big bag on his back.
Ben loves his job.
When you want to send something,
let Ben take it!

PRACTICE

Now read the sentences to a partner. See how your reading improves!

Words to Know

READ AND WRITE

Read each word. Then write it.

1. all _____	2. more _____	3. second _____
4. out _____	5. leave _____	6. enough _____
7. two _____	8. three _____	9. without _____
10. says _____		

Find the new words in the box. Write the words on the lines.

11. These 2 words have 6 letters each. | **12.** These 2 words begin with **s.**

_____ _____   _____ _____

WORD WORK

Work with a partner. Follow the steps.

1 Read aloud each new word in the box.

2 Your partner writes the word.

3 Have your partner read the word to you.

4 Now you write the words on the lines below.

5 Read the words to your partner.

13. _____   18. _____

14. _____   19. _____

15. _____   20. _____

16. _____   21. _____

17. _____   22. _____

BLENDS

Words with Blends

Name each picture. Write the name.

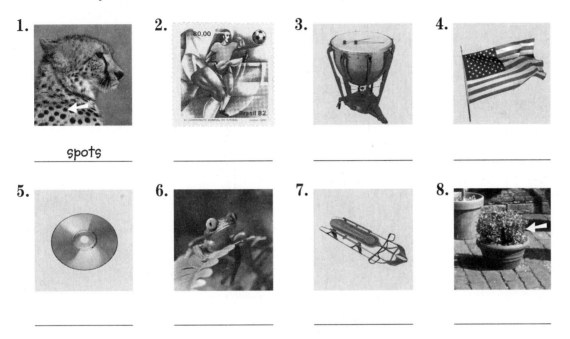

1. _____spots_____

2. _____

3. _____

4. _____

5. _____

6. _____

7. _____

8. _____

Now read the story. Circle the words that go in the chart.
Write them in the chart.

Pack for Camp

Jim packs his bag for camp. He needs enough stuff to last 5 days. He packs:

- 1 tent and a mat to sleep on
- 2 swim trunks for his swim class
- a belt, 4 snacks, 10 socks, 1 brush, and more!

He can smash it all in the bag, but he can not lift the bag! Jim has to pack two bags for camp.

Starts with st	Ends with st
9. _____	13. _____
Starts with tr	**Ends with nt**
10. _____	14. _____
Starts with cl	**Ends with mp**
11. _____	15. ___Camp___
Starts with sn	**Ends with lt**
12. _____	16. _____

DIGRAPHS

Words with Digraphs

Name each picture. Write the name.

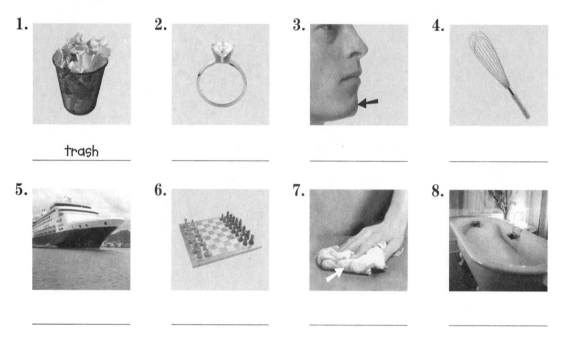

1. trash

2. _____

3. _____

4. _____

5. _____

6. _____

7. _____

8. _____

Now read the story. Circle the words that go in the chart.
Write them in the chart. Write each word one time.

A Trip to (the) (Shop)

Dad and I go out to a shop. I think it
sells great shells. We can bring some to
Mom. I pick six shells and Dad pays
cash. There is one more thing we want
to do – find some fresh fish to eat.
When we go home, Dad gives Mom the
shells. Mom loves them and puts them
on a shelf. What a great day!

Starts with **th**	Starts with **sh**
9. _____the_____	16. _____Shop_____
10. _____	17. _____
11. _____	18. _____
12. _____	
13. _____	
Ends with ng	**Ends with sh**
14. _____	19. _____
15. _____	20. _____
	21. _____

© Hampton-Brown

Build Reading Fluency

When you read, pause between groups of words that go together.

Stan is in **/** a big rush. **//**

Stan has three minutes **/** to catch his plane. **//**

LISTEN AND LEARN TO READ

Listen to the story. When you hear a short pause, write a **/**.
When you hear a long pause, write **//**.

Rush!

Stan is in a big rush. His plane leaves at 2:00 p.m. The clock says 1:57 p.m. Stan has three minutes to catch his plane. That is not very long! He jumps out of the cab and slams the door. Bang! He drops his bag. All of his things fall out of the bag. Then he drops his ticket! A man helps Stan. He picks up the ticket and asks, "When does your plane leave?"

Stan says, "I think it just left without me."

The man looks at Stan's ticket. He grins and tells Stan, "You have enough time. Your plane leaves tomorrow at two."

PRACTICE

Now read the story to a partner. Read groups of words together.
Pause when you see a **/**.

HIGH FREQUENCY WORDS

Words to Know

READ AND WRITE

Read each word. Then write it.

1. people _____	2. come _____	3. by _____
4. animals _____	5. under _____	6. her _____
7. down _____	8. above _____	9. city _____
10. sometimes _____		

WORD WORK

Read each sentence. Find the new words in the box.
Write the words on the lines.

11. This word is the opposite of **go**.

    _____come_____

12. These 4 words are location words.

    _____ _____

    _____ _____

13. These 2 words name living things.

    _____ _____

14. These 2 words start with **c**.

    _____ _____

15. These 2 words end with **y**.

    _____ _____

16. This word has 2 smaller words in it.

    _____

17. These 2 words have **er**.

    _____ _____

18. This word rhymes with **my**.

    _____

Words with Short and Long Vowels

Name each picture. Read the two words. Circle the word
that names the picture.

1.

he / hen

2.

he / help

3.

hi / hit

4.

be / bell

Now read the story. Circle the words with long <u>e</u>.
Then circle the words with short <u>e</u>. Write them in
the chart. Write each word one time.

At Home in (the) City

I like my home in the city. On
Saturdays, Sal and I help at the
library. He sits at the desk. I show
the kids good books. Then I let
them look around without me. At
12:00, we are done. Sometimes we
stop for lunch. Then we go home.
We walk down Grand Road. The
city is so great! We can be home
in two minutes.

Words with long <u>e</u>	Words with short <u>e</u>
5. _____the_____	10. _____help_____
6. _____	11. _____
7. _____	12. _____
8. _____	13. _____
9. _____	14. _____

WORD PATTERNS AND MULTISYLLABIC WORDS

Multisyllabic Words

Read each word. Write how many syllables it has.

1. basket

2

2. pumpkin

3. egg

4. muffin

5. stamp

6. plate

7. napkin

8. bench

Now read the story. Circle the words with two syllables.
Write each word in the chart. Then write the syllables.

A Picnic in the Park

Jan and Chun go on a picnic. Jan
packs lunch in a basket. Chun grabs
a blanket. Then they put on their
helmets and hop on their bikes. They
ride through a tunnel, then up to
Elm Road. They watch out for traffic.
At the park, they see lots of children.
Chun puts the blanket on the grass,
and they sit down. "Let's eat," Jan
says. "Do you want a sandwich?"

	Word	Syllables	
9.	picnic	pic	nic
10.			
11.			
12.			
13.			
14.			
15.			
16.			

Build Reading Fluency

Some sentences tell something. Other sentences show strong feeling.

This sentence tells something. It ends with a period.

> The rabbit is Velvet.

This sentence shows a strong feeling. It ends with an exclamation mark.

> He is so soft!

LISTEN AND LEARN TO READ

Listen to the different kinds of sentences.

Meet Jo

Jo works at the City Animal Hospital. I asked her to tell me about what she does at her job.

I have a great job. I love to help the animals. Look. This cat got hit in traffic. It is so sad when that happens. I had to make her a special bed.

This is Samson. Samson has a bad rash. He has this thing around his neck so he can't bite his skin. Sometimes we play catch. He needs to run a lot.

This rabbit is Velvet. I like to brush him. He is so soft! Velvet had to get his shots. He needs to rest for a day or two. Then he will go home.

So, that is my job. I help hundreds of animals. It is great to see them get well. I miss them when they go home.

PRACTICE

Now read the sentences to a partner.
See how your reading improves!

Words to Know

READ AND WRITE

Read each word. Then write it.

1. our _____	2. watch _____	3. family _____
4. eyes _____	5. father _____	6. really _____
7. head _____	8. mother _____	9. other _____
10. together _____		

WORD WORK

Read the clue. Write the word in the chart.

Then write the word again in the sentence.

What to Look For	Word	Sentence
11. means "dad"	f a t h e r	My ___father___ is an artist.
12. means "mom"	_ _ _ _ _ _	My _____ is a writer.
13. begins with r	_ _ _ _ _ _	We have a _____ big family.
14. begins with to	_ _ _ _ _ _ _ _	We like to be _____.
15. ends with tch	_ _ _ _ _	Sometimes we _____ TV.
16. has her in it	_ _ _ _ _	We do _____ things, too.
17. has 3 letters	_ _ _	Friday is _____ game night.
18. has yes in it	_ _ _ _	I use my _____ to do puzzles.
19. rhymes with bed	_ _ _ _	I think with my _____.
20. begins with fam	_ _ _ _ _ _	My _____ loves games.

LONG VOWELS: *A, I, O, U*

Words with Long Vowels

Name each picture. Write the name.

1.

_____cape_____

2.

_____

3.

_____

4.

_____

5.

_____

6.

_____

7.

_____

8.

_____

Now read the story. Circle the words with long a, i, o, or u.
Write them in the chart. Write each word one time.

Fun with Bill

My brother Bill (drives) a truck

all around the state. When he is home,

he makes life fun.

   Once he put together kites for

all the kids in the family. Bill had to

use long, thin tubes for the frames. The

wings were cloth from a torn robe.

"The kites are cute," he said, "but I

hope we can get them up in the air!"

9. _____	15. _____
10. _____	16. _____
11. _____	17. _____
12. ___drives___	18. _____
13. _____	19. _____
14. _____	20. _____

LONG AND SHORT VOWELS: A, I, O, U

Words with Long and Short Vowels

Name each picture. Read the two words. Circle the word that names the picture.

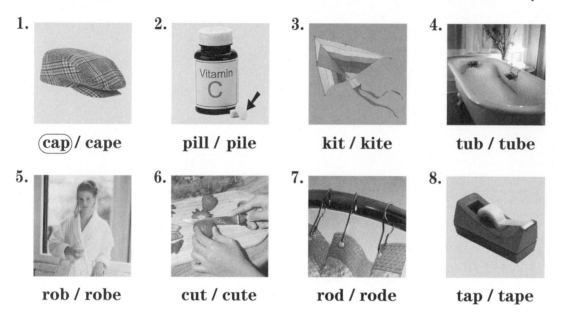

1. (cap) / cape

2. pill / pile

3. kit / kite

4. tub / tube

5. rob / robe

6. cut / cute

7. rod / rode

8. tap / tape

Now read the story. Circle the words with long o or long i. Underline the words with short o or short i. Write them in the chart. Write each word one time.

A Busy (Home)

We are really busy. Here is what a day is like. Mom drives to the pet shop. She must be there by three. The shop closes at three. Then mom stops to get us snacks to eat. Dad helps me fix my bike, and then we scrub the stove. Pam has to watch the baby next door. At the end of the day, we like to sit down and rest. That is when we can all be together again.

9. ___Home___	15. _____
10. _____	16. _____
11. _____	17. _____
12. _____	18. _____
13. _____	19. _____
14. _____	20. _____

COMPREHENSION

Build Reading Fluency

When you read, pause between groups of words that go together.

In Nicaragua, **/** my family made **/** big puppets to sell. **//**

We made the arms **/** from long tubes. **//**

LISTEN AND LEARN TO READ

Listen to the story. When you hear a short pause, write a **/**.
When you hear a long pause, write **//**.

Example: We made the arms **/** from long tubes. **//**

When We Came to Wisconsin

Hi. My name is Pablo Soto. My mother's name is Sandra. We are from Nicaragua.

In Nicaragua, my family made big puppets to sell. The name of one puppet that we made is *La Gigantona*. We made the head of this puppet with paper and paste. We made the eyes of the puppet really big, with long, thick lashes. We made the arms from long tubes. They swing from side to side. We put a white robe and a cute hat on the puppet. People like to watch this big puppet in parades.

PRACTICE

Now read the story to a partner. Use the marks you
made to read groups of words together.

_____

HIGH FREQUENCY WORDS

Words to Know

READ AND WRITE

Read each word. Then write it.

1. once _____
2. world _____
3. below _____
4. or _____
5. river _____
6. water _____
7. places _____
8. always _____
9. through _____
10. important _____

Find the new words. Write the words on the lines.

11. These 4 words have a **w**.

_____   _____

_____   _____

12. These 4 words have 1 syllable.

_____   _____

_____   _____

WORD WORK

Work with a partner. Follow the steps.

1. Read aloud each new word in the box.
2. Your partner writes the words.
3. Have your partner read the words to you.
4. Now you write the words on the lines below.
5. Read the words to your partner.

13. _____
14. _____
15. _____
16. _____
17. _____
18. _____
19. _____
20. _____
21. _____
22. _____

Words with Long <u>a</u>, Long <u>e</u>, and Long <u>o</u>

Read each word. Which picture goes with the word? Write its letter.

1. coast <u>N</u>   2. boat ___   3. train ___   4. braid ___   5. road ___

6. seeds ___   7. paints ___   8. feet ___   9. sail ___   10. tree ___

11. tray ___   12. geese ___   13. crow ___   14. seal ___   15. tea ___

A.   B.   C.   D.   E.

F.   G.   H.   I.   J.

K.   L.   M.   N.   O.

Name each picture below. Which words above have the same long vowel sound as the picture name? Write the words on the lines.

16. train _____

17. _____

18. _____

WORD PATTERNS: *CVC, CVCC, CVVC*

Words with Short and Long Vowels

Name each picture. Read the two words. Circle the word that names the picture.

1. cot / coat

2. tap / tail

3. bed / beach

4. sell / seal

5. pan / paint

6. pens / peas

7. cost / coast

8. rod / road

Now read the story. Circle the words with long <u>a</u>. Underline the words with short <u>a</u>. Write them in the chart. Write each word one time.

Mom to the Rescue!

Nick (always) goes home to see his mom once a year. He <u>packs</u> his gray bag. What if it rains? Nick gets his coat. What if it's hot? Nick gets his swim trunks. He runs to catch the train, but he forgets his bag! Mom meets Nick in Bay City. She asks, "Where is your bag?" At home, Mom looks through the house. Nick waits. Mom comes back with his old clothes!

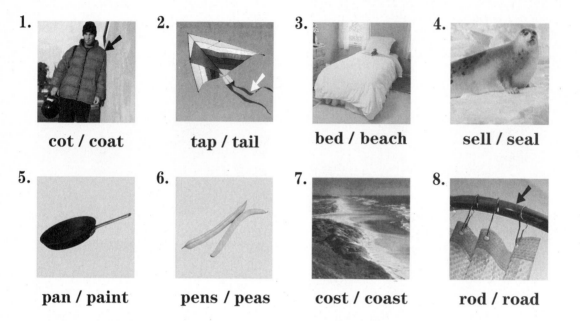

9. ___always___   15. ___packs___

10. _____   16. _____

11. _____   17. _____

12. _____   18. _____

13. _____   19. _____

14. _____   20. _____

MULTISYLLABIC WORDS: COMPOUND WORDS

Multisyllabic Words

Read each word. Write how many syllables it has.

1. weekend

   2

2. crow

3. rowboat

4. train

5. coast

6. seashell

7. sunset

8. stream

Now read the story. Circle the words with two syllables. Write each word in the chart one time. Then write the syllables.

At the (Seashore)

Dean goes to the seashore on weekends. On wet days, Dean wears his raincoat down to the beach. He hunts for seashells and digs for clams. On warm days, he stays on a sailboat with his dad. They sail from sunrise to sunset. Dean loves his weekends at the seashore.

Word	Syllables	
9. seashore	sea	shore
10. _____	_____	_____
11. _____	_____	_____
12. _____	_____	_____
13. _____	_____	_____
14. _____	_____	_____
15. _____	_____	_____

COMPREHENSION

Build Reading Fluency

When you read, pause between groups of words that go together.

Stay in your seat / while we move through the water. //

This is an important place / for animals, / too. //

LISTEN AND LEARN TO READ

Listen to the story. When you hear a short pause, write a **/** .
When you hear a long pause, write a **//** .

Example: This is an important place **/** for animals, **/** too. **//**

Explore a Wetland

Welcome to Black Creek Wetland.
What a great way to spend a
Sunday afternoon! My name is
Jean Clay. I am your guide.
Step into the rowboat. Stay in your seat
while we move through the water.

Canada has many wetlands.
Black Creek Wetland is one of
them. A wetland is a low, wet
place. Rainwater and many
streams keep it wet. Black Creek is
on the shore of Lake Ontario. Plants such
as reeds and cattails grow here. This is an
important place for animals, too. Ducks and
geese lay their eggs here in May.

Sometimes, people drain the water
from wetlands. Then they use the land to
grow wheat or other crops. Not here.
We plan to keep this wetland for the ducks,
geese, and other animals.

PRACTICE

Now read the story to a partner. Read groups of words together. Make a
short pause when you see a **/** . Make a long pause when you see a **//** .

HIGH FREQUENCY WORDS

Words to Know

READ AND WRITE

Read each word. Then write it.

1. saw _____	2. was _____	3. again _____
4. their _____	5. were _____	6. about _____
7. said _____	8. began _____	9. dance _____
10. thought _____		

WORD WORK

Write the answer to each question. Find the new words
in the box. Write the words on the lines.

11. Which 2 words start with **a**?

_____again_____   _____about_____

12. Which 2 words have 3 letters?

_____   _____

13. Which word rhymes with **red**?

_____

14. Which word rhymes with **her**?

_____

15. Which word means "started"?

_____

16. Which word is the past tense of **think**?

_____

17. Which word is the past tense of **see**?

_____

18. Which 5 words have 5 letters each?

_____   _____

_____   _____

_____

19. Which word means "once more"?

_____

20. Which 3 words have 2 syllables?

_____   _____

_____

VERB ENDING: –ED

Verbs with -ed

Read each sentence. Change the word in dark type to tell about the past.

1. Lin and I _____planted_____ seeds.
   (plant)

2. The next day it _____ on our seeds.
   (rain)

3. I _____ her pull the weeds.
   (help)

4. We _____ for the plants to grow.
   (wait)

5. We _____ a lot of peas.
   (pick)

6. We _____ them for our friends.
   (cook)

Now read the story. Circle the words with -ed. Write each
word in the chart one time. Then write the root word.

We (Waited) for the Sun

On Saturday morning it rained . Kim and
I waited for the sun. When it peeked
through the clouds, we ran to the beach.
We saw some birds and hunted for shells
by the water. We cleaned the sand off the
shells and put them in a box. Then we
hunted for tiny crabs in the sand. Kim lifted
one crab so we could see it up close.

Word with -ed	Root Word
7. Waited	wait
8. _____	_____
9. _____	_____
10. _____	_____
11. _____	_____
12. _____	_____

VERB ENDING: –ED

Verbs with -ed

Read each sentence. Change the word in dark type to tell about the past.

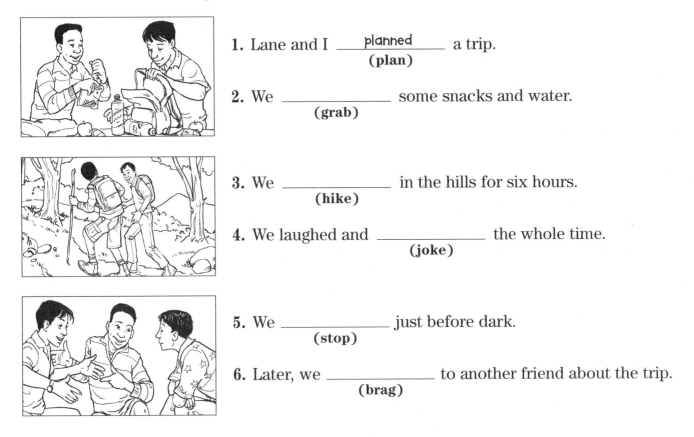

1. Lane and I ___planned___ a trip.
   (**plan**)

2. We _____ some snacks and water.
   (**grab**)

3. We _____ in the hills for six hours.
   (**hike**)

4. We laughed and _____ the whole time.
   (**joke**)

5. We _____ just before dark.
   (**stop**)

6. Later, we _____ to another friend about the trip.
   (**brag**)

Now read the story. Circle the words with **-ed**. Write each
word in the chart one time. Then write the root word.

With a Friend

Ben's feet (dragged) as he jogged in the
park. Sometimes he hated to jog by himself.
He sat down on a bench to rest. Just then
his friend Matt jogged by and waved.

"Matt!" Ben said. "Wait for me!" He
hopped up and ran to catch up with Matt.
He smiled as they ran side by side. It was
more fun to jog with a friend!

Word with –ed	Root Word
7. dragged	drag
8. _____	_____
9. _____	_____
10. _____	_____
11. _____	_____
12. _____	_____

COMPREHENSION

Build Reading Fluency

When you read, pause between groups of words that go together.

She looked at the clock **/** above the stove. **//**

"Veronica has ten more seconds to get here," **/** she said. **//**

LISTEN AND LEARN TO READ

Listen to the story. When you hear a short pause, write a **/** .
When you hear a long pause, write **//** .

Example: "Veronica has ten more seconds to get here," **/** she said. **//**

Eva's Lesson

Eva was mad. She tapped her foot. She looked at the clock above the stove. "Veronica has ten more seconds to get here," she said. Eva waited and waited. Veronica was always late. They had planned to work on their dance for the school show. Eva thought Veronica was not very good. She thought Veronica needed a lot of help.

While she waited, Eva played the CD for their dance. She clapped her hands and kicked to the beat. She began to sing. She kicked again. This time, she kicked too high. She slipped and landed on the rug! Just then, Veronica peeked in the kitchen window. She saw Eva and rushed to help her. Eva smiled and rubbed her leg. "Now I know I was the one who needed help," she joked.

PRACTICE

Now read the story to a partner. Read groups of words together. Make a short pause when you see a **/** . Make a long pause when you see **//** .

Name _____ Date _____

Words to Know

READ AND WRITE

Read each word. Then write it.

1. celebrate _____
2. most _____
3. young _____
4. following _____
5. change _____
6. started _____
7. children _____
8. only _____
9. another _____
10. beginning _____

WORD WORK

Read each clue. Find the new words in the box.
Write the words on the lines.

11. This word starts with **f**.

    _____following_____

12. These 2 words begin with **ch**.

    _____

    _____

13. These 2 words have 4 letters each.

    _____

    _____

14. These words end with **e**.

    _____

    _____

15. These 2 words have **st**.

    _____

    _____

16. These 2 words end with **-ing**.

    _____

    _____

17. This word has the word **other** in it.

    _____

18. This word means "more than one child."

    _____

19. This word is the opposite of **old**.

    _____

20. This word is the opposite of **ended**.

    _____

© Hampton-Brown

Verbs with -ing

Read each sentence. Change the word in dark type to tell what is happening right now.

1. They are ___celebrating___ summer.
(celebrate)

2. Some people are _____ trips.
(take)

3. They are _____ in the pool.
(swim)

4. They are _____ wet.
(get)

5. This family is _____ outside.
(sit)

6. They are _____ a picnic lunch.
(eat)

Now read the story. Circle the words with -ing. Write each word in the chart one time. Then write the root word.

Our School Fair

Our school fair is (beginning) at 2 p.m. We are taking all the games outside. Suddenly, it is raining and we are beginning to get very wet. Most of us are rushing inside. Now we are waiting for the rain to stop. Yes. The sun is shining again. The fair can begin on time.

	Word with -ing	Root Word
7.	beginning	begin
8.		
9.		
10.		
11.		
12.		

Build Reading Fluency

Read the article. Stop when the timer goes off. Mark your
score. Then try it again two more times on different days.

Celebrate the 4th of July

America's birthday is the 4th of July. It is a time to
celebrate. You can have a picnic in the park or watch a
parade. Hundreds of people stand on the street and wait
for the parade to begin. The school bands are first. You
can feel the drums. Next are the fire trucks with wailing
sirens. Then the floats pass by. Boys and girls clap and
yell. They wave red, white, and blue flags.

Celebrating brings people together. They all come to
have a good time. Old people and young children dance
in the streets. Kids eat hot dogs and corn on the cob.
They smile as their dads take pictures. This is the best
way to celebrate the 4th of July!

	Day 1	Day 2	Day 3
Total Words Read in One Minute	————	————	————
Minus Words Missed	————	————	————
Words Read Correctly in One Minute	————	————	————

Words to Know

READ AND WRITE

Read each word. Then write it.

1. life _____	2. been _____	3. sound _____
4. four _____	5. almost _____	6. caused _____
7. often _____	8. never _____	9. could _____
10. between _____		

Answer each question.

11. Which words start with **c**?

_____ _____

12. Which words have the letters **ee** together?

_____ _____

WORD WORK

Read each sentence. Choose a word from the box above.
Then write it in the sentence.

13. My little brother is _____four_____ years old.

14. Kento has been lost only once in his _____ .

15. He _____ always holds Mom's hand.

16. One day Mom said he _____ walk without her.

17. He has always _____ fast, and he ran from her.

18. A clerk heard a _____ .

19. She _____ helps lost children.

20. Kento _____ Mom a lot of worry.

21. He _____ runs from her now.

22. He stays _____ Mom and me!

LONG VOWELS: *IE, IGH; UI, UE*

Words with Long <u>i</u> or Long <u>u</u>

Name each picture. Write the name.

1. _____pie_____

2. _____

3. _____

4. _____

5. _____

6. _____

Now read the story. Circle the words with long <u>i</u> or long <u>u</u>. Write them in the chart. Write each word one time.

The ⟨Right⟩ Thing

Nam often helps at the senior center. He thinks it's the right thing to do. He helps in many ways. He serves pie. He brings in books and takes back the books that are ⟨due.⟩ In art class, Nam helps people cut and glue things. He gets the paints— bright red, yellow, blue. Four nights a year, the center has a big show. Nam wears a suit and tie. The shows are always great!

7. ___right___	12. ___due___
8. _____	13. _____
9. _____	14. _____
10. _____	15. _____
11. _____	

© Hampton-Brown

Build Reading Fluency

Read the article. Stop when the timer goes off. Mark your score. Then try it again two more times on different days.

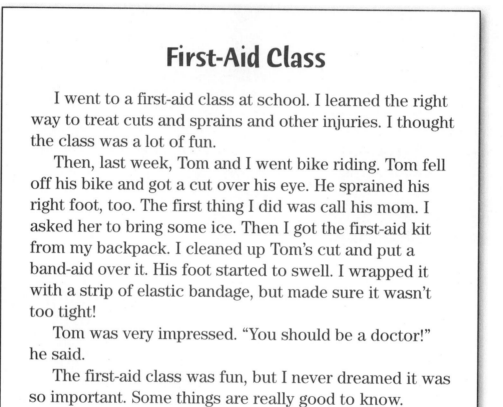

First-Aid Class

I went to a first-aid class at school. I learned the right way to treat cuts and sprains and other injuries. I thought the class was a lot of fun.

Then, last week, Tom and I went bike riding. Tom fell off his bike and got a cut over his eye. He sprained his right foot, too. The first thing I did was call his mom. I asked her to bring some ice. Then I got the first-aid kit from my backpack. I cleaned up Tom's cut and put a band-aid over it. His foot started to swell. I wrapped it with a strip of elastic bandage, but made sure it wasn't too tight!

Tom was very impressed. "You should be a doctor!" he said.

The first-aid class was fun, but I never dreamed it was so important. Some things are really good to know.

	Day 1	Day 2	Day 3
Total Words Read in One Minute	_____	_____	_____
Minus Words Missed	_____	_____	_____
Words Read Correctly in One Minute	_____	_____	_____

Words to Know

READ AND WRITE

Read each word. Then write it.

1. now _____	2. would _____	3. also _____
4. called _____	5. should _____	6. know _____
7. lived _____	8. house _____	9. country _____
10. American _____		

WORD WORK

Read each sentence. Find the new words in the box.
Write the words on the lines.

11. These 2 words rhyme.

_____would_____ _____should_____

12. This word is the opposite of **later**.

_____

13. This word rhymes with **show**.

_____

14. This word rhymes with **cow**.

_____

15. This word has the word **so** in it.

_____

16. This word means almost the same
as **home**.

_____

17. These 2 words are past tense verbs.

_____ _____

18. This word always begins with a
capital letter.

_____

19. These 2 words have a silent **l**.

_____ _____

20. These 2 words have 2 syllables.

_____ _____

R-CONTROLLED VOWELS

Words with R-controlled Vowels

Name each picture. Write the name.

1. ____car____

2. _____

3. _____

4. _____

5. _____

6. _____

7. _____

8. _____

Now read the story. Circle the words that go in the chart. Write them in the chart. Write each word one time.

(Part) of a Team

Melvin is part of a rescue team. When sea birds are hurt after a storm or an oil spill, his team takes them to a yard. First they clean off the oil and dirt. Melvin holds the birds and turns them as he washes off the oil. He stays at the yard from morning until night. It is a hard job, but it is important. When the birds chirp in a happy way, Melvin is also happy. He knows that the birds may survive.

★		
9. ____part____	16. _____	
10. _____	17. _____	
11. _____	18. _____	
	19. _____	
🎺		👧
12. _____	20. _____	
13. _____	21. _____	
14. _____	22. _____	
15. _____		

R-CONTROLLED VOWELS

Words with R-controlled Vowels

Name each picture. Write the name.

1. 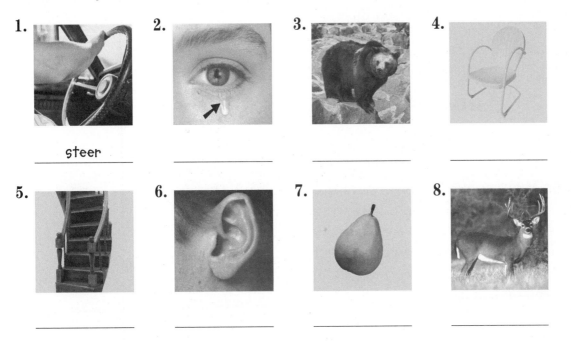 steer

2.

3.

4.

5.

6.

7.

8.

Now read the story. Circle the words that go in the chart.
Write them in the chart.

A Great Guy

Lee always (cheers) people up. One
year, when I was sick, he gave me a
toy deer. It was so funny. It had a wig
with long hair and a pair of
sunglasses. Last year, Lee planted
tomatoes near his house. He gave my
mom a bag of big, bright tomatoes.
Lee also helps a family in another
country. He sends them socks to
wear. He brings stuffed bears to kids
in Children's Hospital.

9. _____cheers_____	13. _____
10. _____	14. _____
11. _____	15. _____
12. _____	16. _____

COMPREHENSION

Build Reading Fluency

Read the article. Stop when the timer goes off. Mark your score.
Then try it again two more times on different days.

Another Kid Helps Kids

Kimmie Weeks started making a difference when he was 10. The year was 1991. His country, Liberia, was at war. Many homes and schools were destroyed. Hundreds of children had no food. Many were sick. The fighting was so bad, children were trained to be soldiers. No one seemed to know what to do. Kimmie felt he had to help.

He and other kids started cleaning the streets. They picked up bricks, stones, and other trash left after the fighting. Then he started speaking on the radio. He said that children should not fight in war. His speeches helped. In 1996, Liberia stopped training children to fight.

Kimmie is now a young man. He is still helping the children of his country. He raises money to open more schools. Today, many children have better lives thanks to Kimmie Weeks.

	Day 1	Day 2	Day 3
Total Words Read in One Minute	_____	_____	_____
Minus Words Missed	_____	_____	_____
Words Read Correctly in One Minute	_____	_____	_____

Words to Know

READ AND WRITE

Read each word. Then write it.

1. story _____	2. oil _____	3. why _____
4. found _____	5. over _____	6. try _____
7. because _____	8. away _____	9. few _____
10. mountains _____		

Answer each question.

11. Which words begin with the letter **f**?

_____ _____

12. Which words rhyme with **by**?

_____ _____

WORD WORK

Work with a partner. Follow the steps.

1. Read aloud each new word in the box.

2. Your partner writes the words.

3. Have your partner read the words to you.

4. Now you write the words on the lines below.

5. Read the words to your partner.

13. _____	18. _____
14. _____	19. _____
15. _____	20. _____
16. _____	21. _____
17. _____	22. _____

SYLLABLE TYPES

Types of Syllables

Name each picture. Read the two words.
Circle the word that names the picture.

1. marker / (market)

2. letter / winter

3. perfume / person

4. under / ladder

5. garden / garter

6. timber / corner

7. hammer / summer

8. butter / pepper

Now read the story. Then read each word in the chart.
Write the syllables in the word.

My Sister Meg

My sister Meg should live on a farm and drive a tractor. She loves to grow things! She gets perfect seeds at the market and plants them in our garden. She plants peppers for Dad and turnips for Mom. Gram asks for butter beans. Meg plants a few things for herself: plums and peas. We all help harvest what she grows. Then we cook supper. Food from the garden always tastes better!

Words	Syllables	
9. sister	sis	ter
10. perfect	_____	_____
11. garden	_____	_____
12. peppers	_____	_____
13. turnips	_____	_____
14. butter	_____	_____
15. harvest	_____	_____
16. supper	_____	_____

© Hampton-Brown

Build Reading Fluency

**Read the article. Stop when the timer goes off. Mark your score.
Then try it again two more times on different days.**

A Robin's Nest

The American robin is the biggest member of the thrush family. It is not hard to spot a robin. It is gray with a black head. The throat is white with black streaks. The chest is an orange-red.

After winter, most birds make new nests. Many birds use twigs and leaves to make their nests. A robin uses twigs, leaves, spring grasses, and mud. They use the mud to make the nest strong. Then they line the nest with grass. The grass makes the nest soft and warm for the eggs. A robin lays four or five eggs each spring. The eggs are light blue without any spots.

Robins are quite at home living near people, so you may find their nests in parks or gardens. Look for them in spring!

	Day 1	Day 2	Day 3
Total Words Read in One Minute	_____	_____	_____
Minus Words Missed	_____	_____	_____
Words Read Correctly in One Minute	_____	_____	_____

Words to Know

READ AND WRITE

Read each word. Then write it.

1. words _____	2. back _____	3. example _____
4. ever _____	5. miss _____	6. along _____
7. much _____	8. news _____	9. before _____
10. question _____		

WORD WORK

Read the clue. Write the word in the chart.

Then write the word again in the sentence.

What to Look For	Word	Sentence
11. ends with **ss**	m i s s	I __miss__ my friend.
12. has a **v**	_ _ _ _	He's the best friend I _____ had.
13. means "a lot"	_ _ _ _	I like him so _____.
14. has an **x**	_ _ _ _ _ _ _	Ted is an _____ of a true friend.
15. tells when	_ _ _ _ _ _	He left _____ summer.
16. ends with **ng**	_ _ _ _ _	I went _____ to say good-bye.
17. has **ew**	_ _ _ _	Now I send Ted my _____.
18. begins with **w**	_ _ _ _ _	I write lots of _____.
19. ends with **tion**	_ _ _ _ _ _ _ _	I ask him one _____.
20. ends with **ck**	_ _ _ _	When will you come _____?

WORDS WITH Y

Words with y

Read each word. Tell if the letter y is a vowel or a consonant.

1.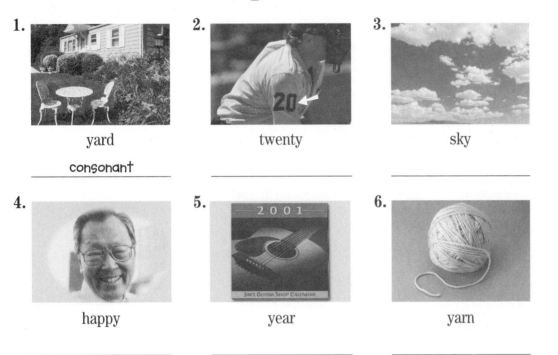

yard

_____consonant_____

2.

twenty

_____

3.

sky

_____

4.

happy

_____

5.

year

_____

6.

yarn

_____

Read the story. Circle the words with y. Write the words in the chart. Write each word one time.

(Why) I Admire Raoul Wallenburg

My class read about World War II. In one (story) a man risked his life to save others. He could not be happy while other people suffered so much. He gave a lot of lucky people passports so that they could escape. He helped other people find places to hide. By the end of the war, he had helped 100,000 people.

7. ___Why___	10. ___story___
8. _____	11. _____
9. _____	12. _____

WORDS WITH Y

Plurals: y + s, y to i + es

Read each sentence. Change the word in dark type to name more than one.

1. I have many ___hobbies___ .
   (**hobby**)

2. On some _____ , I make model planes from
   (**day**)
   World War II.

3. My _____ like to help me.
   (**buddy**)

4. We eat lunch on _____ as we work.
   (**tray**)

5. We tell each other _____ about the planes.
   (**story**)

6. We pretend the planes are still up in the _____ .
   (**sky**)

Now read the story. Circle the plurals that end in -ys and -ies.
Write each word in the chart. Then write the root word.

Dad's Favorite Hobby

My dad has many (hobbies.) The hobby
he likes best is history. He likes to read
about England and other countries in
World War II. Sometimes he tells me
stories about those days. Dad has other
ways to learn about history. For example,
he collects old things, like newspapers,
stamps, and coins from the forties.

Word that Ends in -ys or -ies	Root Word
7. ___hobbies___	___hobby___
8. _____	_____
9. _____	_____
10. _____	_____
11. _____	_____
12. _____	_____

© Hampton-Brown

READING FLUENCY

Build Reading Fluency

Read the letter. Stop when the timer goes off. Mark your score.
Then try it again two more times on different days.

June 25, 1937
Oshkosh, Wisconsin

Dear Sister,

Thank you for the letter. I love reading the news from Poland.

Well, my first year in America has not been easy. This is a fine country, but I was not always happy. It was hard to find a job. I had no money for a long time. Uncle Jedrick paid for the things I needed. Today my life is much better! I work six days a week in a factory. Now I can help Uncle Jedrick pay for food. I am also saving a few pennies each week. This summer I will have money to send to Mom.

I miss you so much! I wait for the day you and Mom can come to America. Then we will all be together again! Until then, think of me and write often!

Love,
Konrad

	Day 1	Day 2	Day 3
Total Words Read in One Minute	_____	_____	_____
Minus Words Missed	_____	_____	_____
Words Read Correctly in One Minute	_____	_____	_____

HIGH FREQUENCY WORDS

Words to Know

READ AND WRITE

Read each word. Then write it.

1. each _____	2. sentence _____	3. as _____
4. idea _____	5. plants _____	6. into _____
7. made _____	8. seemed _____	9. but _____
10. until _____		

WORD WORK

Read each sentence. Find the new words in the box.
Write the words on the lines.

11. These 2 words start with **s**.

   _____sentence_____   _____seemed_____

12. This word is the first in ABC order.

   _____

13. These 2 words have **ea**.

   _____ _____

14. This word names things that grow.

   _____

15. These 2 words have a **u**.

   _____ _____

16. These 4 words have 4 letters each.

   _____ _____

   _____ _____

17. This word is the last in ABC order.

   _____

18. This word is the opposite of **out of**.

   _____

19. These 2 words have an **m**.

   _____ _____

20. These 2 words are things you write.

   _____ _____

Name _____ Date _____

Words with <u>oi</u>, <u>oy</u>, <u>ou</u>, and <u>ow</u>

Read each word. Which picture goes with the word? Write its letter.

1. boil _G_   2. couch ___   3. owl ___   4. crown ___   5. house ___

6. cloud ___   7. boy ___   8. crowd ___   9. coin ___   10. points ___

11. proud ___   12. soil ___   13. mouse ___   14. frown ___   15. toys ___

A. B. C. D. E.

F. G. H. I. J.

K. L. M. N. O.

Read each word. Find the word or words above that have the same vowel sound _and_ spelling. Write the words on the lines.

16. join   17. joy   18. loud   19. clown

___boil___   _____   _____   _____

_____   _____   _____   _____

_____   _____   _____

_____   _____

VARIANT VOWELS

Words with <u>oo</u>, <u>ew</u>, <u>au</u>, <u>aw</u>, <u>al</u>, and <u>all</u>

Read each word. Which picture goes with the word? Write its letter.

1. mall __H__   2. saw __   3. broom __   4. salt __   5. screw __

6. hawk __   7. author __   8. moon __   9. stew __   10. hall __

11. draw __   12. boots __   13. laundry __   14. pool __   15. ball __

A.   B.   C.   D.   E.

F.   G.   H.   I.   J.

K.   L.   M.   N.   O.

Read each word. Find the words above that have the same sound _and_ spelling. Write the words on the lines.

16. cool __broom__   17. awful _____   18. small _____

_____   _____   _____

_____   _____   _____

_____

19. chew _____   20. haunted _____   21. also _____

_____

Build Reading Fluency

Read the story. Stop when the timer goes off. Mark your score. Then try it again two more times on different days.

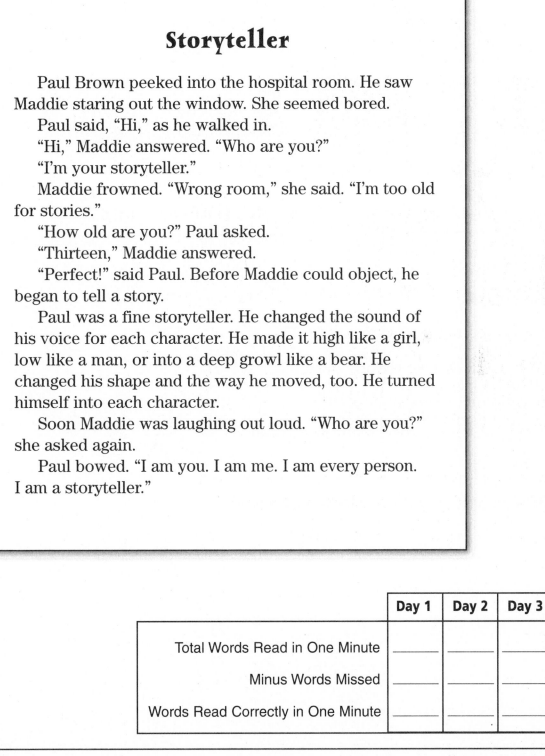

Storyteller

Paul Brown peeked into the hospital room. He saw Maddie staring out the window. She seemed bored.

Paul said, "Hi," as he walked in.

"Hi," Maddie answered. "Who are you?"

"I'm your storyteller."

Maddie frowned. "Wrong room," she said. "I'm too old for stories."

"How old are you?" Paul asked.

"Thirteen," Maddie answered.

"Perfect!" said Paul. Before Maddie could object, he began to tell a story.

Paul was a fine storyteller. He changed the sound of his voice for each character. He made it high like a girl, low like a man, or into a deep growl like a bear. He changed his shape and the way he moved, too. He turned himself into each character.

Soon Maddie was laughing out loud. "Who are you?" she asked again.

Paul bowed. "I am you. I am me. I am every person. I am a storyteller."

	Day 1	Day 2	Day 3
Total Words Read in One Minute	_____	_____	_____
Minus Words Missed	_____	_____	_____
Words Read Correctly in One Minute	_____	_____	_____

HIGH FREQUENCY WORDS

Words to Know

READ AND WRITE

Read each word. Then write it.

1. talked _____	2. asked _____	3. if _____
4. walked _____	5. while _____	6. such _____
7. trees _____	8. even _____	9. air _____
10. friends _____		

Answer each question.

11. Which words have 4 letters?

_____ _____

12. Which words rhyme?

_____ _____

WORD WORK

Work with a partner. Follow the steps.

1 Read aloud each new word in the box.

2 Your partner writes the words.

3 Have your partner read the words to you.

4 Now you write the words on the lines below.

5 Read the words to your partner.

13. _____   18. _____

14. _____   19. _____

15. _____   20. _____

16. _____   21. _____

17. _____   22. _____

Name _____   Date _____

Words with Hard and Soft <u>c</u> or <u>g</u>

Read each word. Find the picture that goes with the word. Write its letter.

1. gum ⎿__   2. garden ___   3. gem ___   4. race ___

5. city ___   6. goat ___   7. cones ___   8. cent ___

9. gate ___   10. cut ___   11. pages ___   12. cap ___

A.   B. C. D.

E. F. G. H.

I. J. K. L.

Name each picture below. Find the word or words in which the
<u>c</u> or <u>g</u> makes the same sound. Write the words on the lines.

13. cones _____
_____

14. _____
_____

15. _____
_____

16. _____
_____

VARIANT VOWELS AND SILENT CONSONANTS

Words with /o͝o/ or Silent Consonants

Name each picture. Write the name.

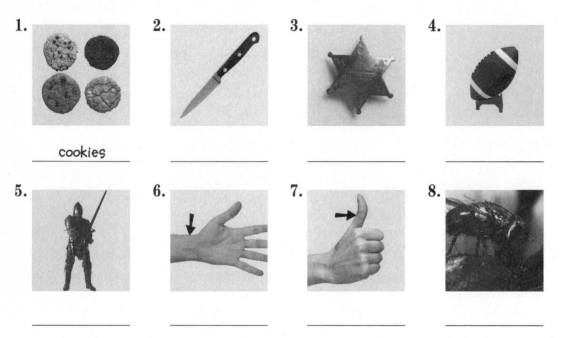

1. cookies

2. _____

3. _____

4. _____

5. _____

6. _____

7. _____

8. _____

Now read the story. Circle the words with /o͝o/ or silent consonants. Write them in the chart. Write each word one time.

My Very Best

I love to play (football.) I was a good player, but Coach said, "I (know) you can do better." So one day I walked to the library to get a book about football. I stood in the sports section a long time and looked at many books. Finally, I took one that had lots of tips: how to dodge other players, throw, and even how to keep your knees from getting wrecked. Thanks to that book, I don't do anything wrong now. Coach and my friends give me the thumbs up!

9. football	15. know
10. _____	16. _____
11. _____	17. _____
12. _____	18. _____
13. _____	19. _____
14. _____	20. _____

© Hampton-Brown

COMPREHENSION

Build Reading Fluency

Read the article. Stop when the timer goes off. Mark your score.
Then try it again two more times on different days.

Hard Ice

Ice is hard. When you fall on ice, you really feel it. My name is Sonny Chen. I'm an ice skater, so I know what I'm talking about. I started skating when I was three years old. Back then, I spent more time falling on the ice than skating. Yet I loved the sport even then.

When I was ten, I learned a move called "the axel." To do this move, I go forward on the outside edge of one skate. After gaining speed, I leap off the ice and spin in the air. I land on the outside edge of the other skate. It took me a long time to get it right the first time. Then, suddenly, I nailed it! I made a perfect landing! What a great feeling that was. It was worth ten thousand falls, even on hard ice.

	Day 1	Day 2	Day 3
Total Words Read in One Minute	_____	_____	_____
Minus Words Missed	_____	_____	_____
Words Read Correctly in One Minute	_____	_____	_____

Words to Know

READ AND WRITE

Read each word. Then write it.

1. earth _____	2. state _____	3. form _____
4. million _____	5. than _____	6. sea _____
7. miles _____	8. near _____	9. high _____
10. explore _____		

Answer each question.

11. Which words have two syllables?

_____ _____

12. Which words have **th**?

_____ _____

WORD WORK

Read each sentence. Choose a word from the box above.
Then write it in the sentence.

13. Caves are hollow places in the ____*earth*____ .

14. They are found inland and by the _____ .

15. Some caves are bigger _____ others.

16. Mammoth Cave is in the _____ of Kentucky.

17. It is _____ the city of Bowling Green.

18. The cave is under a _____ ridge of limestone.

19. It is over 340 _____ long.

20. Rivers under the ground _____ lakes inside the cave.

21. Mammoth Cave is over one _____ years old.

22. People like to _____ Mammoth Cave.

Mammoth Cave

MULTISYLLABIC WORDS

Multisyllabic Words

Read each word. Write how many syllables it has.

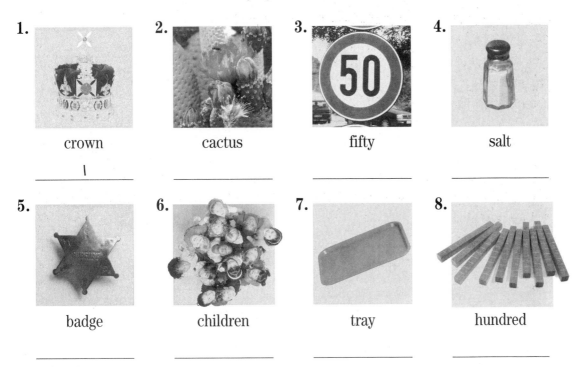

1. crown

_____1_____

2. cactus

_____

3. fifty

_____

4. salt

_____

5. badge

_____

6. children

_____

7. tray

_____

8. hundred

_____

Now read the story. Circle the words with two syllables. Write each word in the chart. Then write the syllables in the word. Write each word one time.

The Old Days

My class went to a (hamlet) near Boston. A hamlet is a small town. We learned how children and their folks lived in the past. In the hamlet, actors dress in costumes and do things by hand. We watched a girl in a long dress churn butter. We saw a man make nails. Life was hard hundreds of years ago. When we got back to school, we had a contest to see who knew the most facts.

	Word	Syllables	
9.	hamlet	ham	let
10.			
11.			
12.			
13.			
14.			
15.			
16.			

Multisyllabic Words

Read each word. Write how many syllables it has.

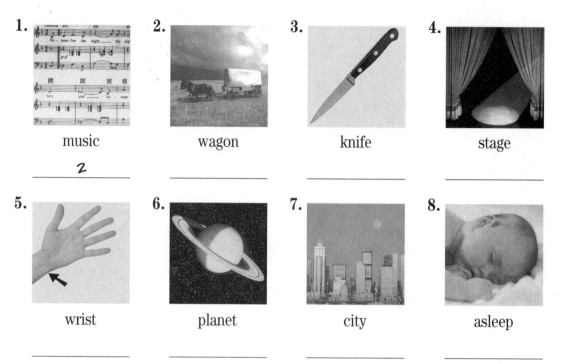

1. music

   2

2. wagon

3. knife

4. stage

5. wrist

6. planet

7. city

8. asleep

**Now read the story. Then read each word in the chart.
Write the syllables in the word.**

Niagara Falls

Niagara Falls is near Buffalo, New York. Last week, my mom and I went to visit the falls. We stayed in a cozy cabin. We rode up the river in a boat. The waterfalls amazed me. The roar of the falls is so loud! The falls are about 175 feet high. They formed about 12,000 years ago. Next time, you should come along!

Words	Syllables	
9. visit	vis	it
10. cozy	_____	_____
11. cabin	_____	_____
12. about	_____	_____
13. ago	_____	_____
14. along	_____	_____

Build Reading Fluency

Read the article. Stop when the timer goes off. Mark your score.
Then try it again two more times on different days.

The Pony Express Trail

Before 1860, it took three weeks to carry mail across the United States. It traveled slowly by boat and by stage coach. Then the U.S. started a new mail service. It was called the Pony Express. Many boys worked for the Pony Express. They rode fast ponies between the state of Missouri and the California coast. Each rider rode about 75 miles, changing ponies along the way. After 75 miles, another rider would take the mailbag. The riders rode day and night. They rode through heat, rain, and snow. They traveled 1,966 miles across plains, deserts, and high mountains. The entire trip took ten days. The riders were paid $100 to $150 a month. That was a lot of money in 1860, and the riders earned every penny of it.

	Day 1	Day 2	Day 3
Total Words Read in One Minute	_____	_____	_____
Minus Words Missed	_____	_____	_____
Words Read Correctly in One Minute	_____	_____	_____

Words to Know

READ AND WRITE

Read each word. Then write it.

1. healthy _____	2. weigh _____	3. cold _____
4. outdoors _____	5. indoors _____	6. warm _____
7. special _____	8. own _____	9. any _____
10. beautiful _____		

WORD WORK

Read the clue. Write the word in the chart.

Then write the word again in the sentence.

What to Look For	Word	Sentence
11. starts with **sp**	s p e c i a l	Fall is a _special_ time.
12. means "outside"	_ _ _ _ _ _ _ _	I work _____ under the sky.
13. means "belongs to me"	_ _ _	I want my _____ garden.
14. ends with **-ful**	_ _ _ _ _ _ _ _ _	My berries are _____.
15. is the opposite of **cool**	_ _ _ _	They love the _____ sun.
16. means "not sick"	_ _ _ _ _ _ _	The pumpkins are _____, too.
17. rhymes with **say**	_ _ _ _ _	They can _____ 20 pounds.
18. is the opposite of **hot**	_ _ _ _	Today is windy and _____.
19. rhymes with **many**	_ _ _	There isn't _____ sun.
20. means "inside"	_ _ _ _ _ _ _	So I stay _____ and read.

Suffixes: -ly, -y

The suffix -ly changes an adjective to an adverb. The suffix -y changes a noun to an adjective. Read each sentence. Add -ly or -y to the word in dark type to complete the sentence.

1.

The sun is **bright**. It shines ___brightly___ .

2.

The drums are **loud**. The boy plays _____ .

3.

This room is a **mess**. It is ___messy___ .

4.

The machine digs up **dirt**. It gets _____ .

5.

He is a **safe** rider. He rides _____ .

6.

The boy plays in the **sand**. He gets _____ .

Now read the story. Circle each word with the suffix -ly or -y . Write the words in the chart. Then write the root words.

In the Garden

Kim's alarm clock rang loudly. She still felt sleepy! She dressed quickly in old pants and tiptoed softly into the garden. It was a warm, windy day. Kim bent down and dug in the rocky soil. Suddenly her hand hit something. She dug a little more and discovered a big, brown potato. Kim pulled it out of the dirt. "It must weigh five pounds," she thought. "It could make a healthy meal for six people."

Word with -ly	Root Word
7. loudly	loud
8. _____	_____
9. _____	_____
10. _____	_____

Word with -y	Root Word
11. _____	_____
12. _____	_____
13. _____	_____
14. _____	_____

SUFFIXES

Suffixes: -ful, -less

The suffix -ful means "full of." The suffix -less means "without." Add -ful or -less
to each word to make a new word. Write the word that goes with each picture.

1. end_less___

2. fear_____

3. use_____

4. peace_ful___

5. grace_____

6. harm_____

Now read the story. Circle each word with the suffix -ful or -less.
Write the words in the chart. Then write the root words.

Sun and Wind

Mike looked at his grape vines. The
hot sun beat down on the plants. A warm
wind began to blow. Mike was worried
because wind can be(harmful)to grapes.
The wind blew for days. It seemed
endless. "I hope my vines survive," Mike
thought. "I wish I could do something,
but I am helpless." He felt so useless. At
last, the wind stopped. It was peaceful
again. The grape vines still looked
healthy. Mike felt very thankful.

Word with -ful	Root Word
7. ___harmful___	harm
8. _____	_____
9. _____	_____

Word with -less	Root Word
10. _____	_____
11. _____	_____
12. _____	_____

PREFIXES

Prefixes: re-, un-

The prefix re- can mean "again." The prefix un- can mean "not" or
"the opposite of." Add re- or un- to each word to make a new word.
Write the word that goes with the picture.

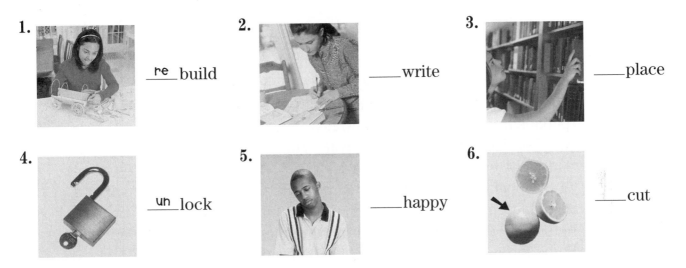

1. _re_ build

2. ____write

3. ____place

4. _un_ lock

5. ____happy

6. ____cut

Now read the story. Circle each word with the prefix re- or un-.
Write the words in the chart. Then write the root words.

Miller's Farm

At Miller's Farm you can (relive) the
past. You can taste fresh, unsalted
peanuts. You can also make your own
peanut butter. First, untie a big sack
and take some peanuts. Be sure to
retie the sack. Take off the shells,
then put the peanuts in a grinder.
Grind the peanuts to make peanut
butter. Uncover a jar and fill it. Put
the cover on the jar. Refill the grinder
to make more peanut butter.

Word with re-		Root Word
7. ____relive____		live
8. _____		_____
9. _____		_____

Word with un-		Root Word
10. _____		_____
11. _____		_____
12. _____		_____

COMPREHENSION

Build Reading Fluency

Read the article. Stop when the timer goes off. Mark your score.
Then try it again two more times on different days.

Farmers' Market

It is 5 a.m. A pickup truck drives slowly into a parking lot. A farmer quickly sets up a table outdoors. She unloads freshly picked fruit and healthy green beans. Another driver unloads crusty rolls and tasty pies. Suddenly the lot fills with trucks.

Shoppers are eagerly arriving now. Farmers quickly untie bags of corn and stack up endless piles of crunchy nuts. They display jars of wonderful homemade jams. Some farmers proudly offer free samples. Lucky shoppers taste the tomatoes. They are really flavorful— unlike the tasteless tomatoes you find in some stores.

At 4 p.m., the farmers reload their trucks. The lot is silent again. Tomorrow, it may be warm, cold, rainy, or windy. No matter what the weather may be, the farmers' market will reopen tomorrow in another town.

	Day 1	Day 2	Day 3
Total Words Read in One Minute	_____	_____	_____
Minus Words Missed	_____	_____	_____
Words Read Correctly in One Minute	_____	_____	_____

HIGH FREQUENCY WORDS

Words to Know

READ AND WRITE

Read each word. Then write it.

1. right _____
2. close _____
3. show _____
4. watch _____
5. kind _____

Answer each question.

6. Which 3 words name actions?

_____   _____

_____

7. Which 2 words also name things?

_____   _____

WORD WORK

Read each question. Find the new words in the box.
Write the words on the lines.

8. Which word is the opposite of **left**?

_____

9. Which 2 words can be both a verb and a noun?

_____   _____

10. Which word means "near"?

_____

11. Which 2 words can be adjectives?

_____   _____

12. Which word is the opposite of **hide**?

_____

13. Which word means "type of"?

_____

14. Which word is the opposite of **open**?

_____

15. Which word means "look at"?

_____

MULTISYLLABIC WORDS

Types of Syllables

Name each picture. Read the two words.
Circle the word that names the picture.

1. middle / (pickle)

2. table / little

3. circle / gentle

4. beetle / eagle

5. apple / able

6. candle / huddle

7. twinkle / title

8. turtle / purple

Now read the story. Circle the words with a consonant + <u>le</u>.
Write them in the chart.

A Native American (Fable)

Native Americans tell stories about Coyote. In one story, Coyote sees a (little) star that twinkles like a candle. "Come close!" Coyote yells. "I want to dance with you." The star floats down and he grabs it. He soars like an eagle, high over Table Rock. He isn't able to hang on. His hands slip and he tumbles down. Splat! He lands by a beetle. What did Coyote learn? It's simple: You can't do everything you want.

Long Vowel in First Syllable	Short Vowel in First Syllable
9. ___Fable___	14. ___little___
10. _____	15. _____
11. _____	16. _____
12. _____	17. _____
13. _____	18. _____

Types of Syllables

Name each picture. Read the two words. Circle the word
that names the picture.

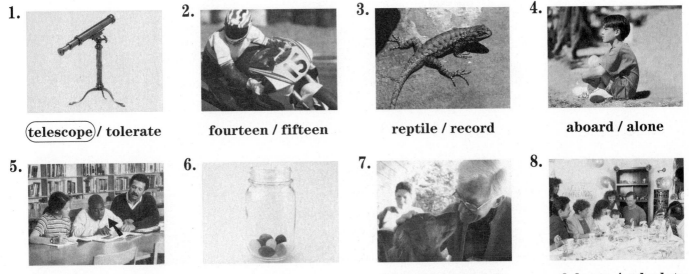

1. (telescope) / tolerate

2. fourteen / fifteen

3. reptile / record

4. aboard / alone

5. beneath / between

6. remain / repeat

7. fearful / faithful

8. celebrate / calculate

Now read the story. Circle the two-syllable words.
Find the vowel pattern. Write each word in the chart.
Write each word one time.

Apollo (Thirteen)

In 1970, a space (capsule) tried to reach the

moon. However, a mistake caused two air tanks

to explode. No one knew the reason for the

mistake. Yet the craft could not go to the moon.

The astronauts had to survive, so they released

the tanks. Teams on Earth watched and helped

the crew succeed. They exclaimed joyfully

when the astronauts got home alive.

Two Vowels Work Together	Vowel and _e_ Work Together
9. ___Thirteen___	14. ___capsule___
10. _____	15. _____
11. _____	16. _____
12. _____	17. _____
13. _____	18. _____

Multisyllabic Words

Read each word. Write how many syllables it has.

1. eagle
   2

2. unbuckle

3. faithful

4. superstar

5. telescope

6. replace

7. candle

8. unafraid

Now read the story. Circle the words with more than one syllable. Write each word in the chart one time. Then write the syllables in the word.

The (Republic) of Blues

My band is called The Republic of Blues. A lot of faithful fans come to our shows. They love our kind of music. I play the steel drums and Clive sings. He likes to rearrange old songs, too. I like his simple love songs best. I hope he does not leave the band. I would be so unhappy. I don't think I could replace him. I hope we will both be stars one day!

Word	Syllables		
9. Republic	Re	pub	lic
10. _____	___	___	
11. _____	___	___	
12. _____	___	___	___
13. _____	___	___	
14. _____	___	___	
15. _____	___	___	

COMPREHENSION

Build Reading Fluency

Read the myth. Stop when the timer goes off. Mark your score. Then try it again two more times on different days.

A Tale from Greece

When the sun is very hot, the people of Greece remember an old tale. It is about an inventor named Daedalus. The king was angry with Daedalus because he helped destroy the king's monster bull. The king punished him by locking him and his son Icarus inside a high tower.

Daedalus planned a clever escape. He plucked feathers from birds that visited the tower. He used candle wax to glue the feathers onto wooden frames. In this way, he made two pairs of wings.

When they put on the wings, Daedalus told Icarus, "Promise me you will not fly too high. If you do, the sun will melt the wax."

Icarus nodded, but when he flew into the sky, the boy forgot his promise. He flew higher and higher. Daedalus called out, but his cry came too late. The boy's wings melted, and he fell into the sea.

	Day 1	Day 2	Day 3
Total Words Read in One Minute	_____	_____	_____
Minus Words Missed	_____	_____	_____
Words Read Correctly in One Minute	_____	_____	_____

COMPREHENSION

Timed Reading Chart

How many words did you read correctly for each selection?
Complete the chart to show your scores for each day.

	Celebrate the 4th of July	First-Aid Class	Another Kid Helps Kids	A Robin's Nest	June 25, 1937	Storyteller	Hard Ice	The Pony Express Trail	Farmers' Market	A Tale from Greece
	page 73	page 76	page 80	page 83	page 87	page 91	page 95	page 99	page 104	page 109

Decodable Stories

NOT a Good Day!

This is not a good day!

Look Back at Not a Good Day!

CHECK YOUR UNDERSTANDING

1. What is the first thing that happens to the girl?

2. How does the girl feel about her lunch?

3. Why does the girl say, "This is not a good day!"?

WORD WORK: Short a, Short o

Circle all the words in the story with the short a sound. Underline all the words with the short o sound. Then make a chart of the words. Write each word one time.

Short a	Short o
at	not

Unit 1 | Glad to Meet You!

I go to school at 8:00.

I have ham for lunch. I do not like ham. Now I am sad.

First I have English class. I do not have my school bag. It is at home.

Next I have to jog in P.E. It is too hot!

My mom is mad.

Then my dad comes to school in the van. He has my bag.

4

5

Short i, Short u, ch, and tch

Catch some popcorn, Mom!

It is such a mess! Mom does not like it a bit. Jim just grins.

Look Back at *Pop!*

CHECK YOUR UNDERSTANDING

1. Think about what happens to Jim. Draw a box. In it, write what Jim does first.

Jim hits the TV switch.

Draw 5 more boxes. Tell what else Jim does.

2. Why does the popcorn pop out of the microwave?

WORD WORK: *ch* and *tch*

Look for words with *ch* or *tch*. Write the words in a list.

switch bunch

Unit 2 | Set the Table

Jim hits the TV switch.

Popcorn fills the room!

Oh, no!

Then he hunts for something to eat. There is just a bunch of old stuff, but he does see a bag of . . .

Popcorn! It is fast to make.

Jim looks in the microwave. He can see a rip in the bag. Jim opens the microwave.

Short e, sh, ck, and Double Consonants

Fred at Work

© Hampton-Brown

At last, the long day ends.
Mom has one last job for Fred.

Fred! Help me carry these bags.

Where is Fred? He is in bed! *Zzzzzzz.*

Look Back at *Fred at Work*

CHECK YOUR UNDERSTANDING

1. Where does Fred work?
2. How does he help people?
3. Why is Fred in bed at the end of the story?

WORD WORK: Short e, sh, ck, and Double Consonants

Circle all the words in the story with the short e sound. Underline all the words in the story with sh, ck, or a double consonant. Compare your list to a partner's list. Did you miss any words?

Fred loves his job on the docks. He gets to do many different things.

Fred takes the trash to the bin.

From Last to First

Two days later, there is a track meet. This time, Fran is not last. Fran is first.

Go, Fran!

Look Back at *From Last to First*

CHECK YOUR UNDERSTANDING

1. Think about the story. What is Fran's problem?

2. How does she solve the problem?

3. Why is the story called *From Last to First*?

WORD WORK: Blends and Digraphs

Circle all the words in the story that have two consonants together. Make a chart. If each consonant has a sound, write the word in the first column. If the two consonants make one sound, write the word in the second column.

Two Sounds	One Sound
belt	rush

It is 7:00 a.m. on a school day. Fran is still in bed.

Fran! It is 7:00 a.m.!

BANG! BANG!

Fran does not rush.

Fran jumps on the bottom step. She is the last one on the bus.

She did it!

Good job!

A City Food Festival

We can't stop yet!

You go. I can't move. No more food festivals for me.

Look Back at A City Food Festival

CHECK YOUR UNDERSTANDING

1. Where do Pedro and Ekram go?

2. What do they do there?

3. How does the story end?

WORD WORK: Multisyllabic Words

Find these words in the story.

happens	hundreds
basket	napkin
pumpkin	sandwich

Circle the words. Then write the syllables in each word.

happens   hap pens

Long Vowels: *a, i, o, u*

At Home

Grandmother likes all the things we do for her. She even likes my brother's drums.

CRASH!

BANG!

Look Back at *At Home*

CHECK YOUR UNDERSTANDING

1. What does each person in the family do for Grandmother?

2. How can you tell that Grandmother feels glad?

3. What are some special things that you do for your family?

WORD WORK: Long Vowels

Find all the words with a long vowel and silent e.

Make a list. Compare your list to your partner's list. Read the two lists aloud. Did you find the same words?

hope	bake
time	tune

My grandmother is here from Japan. Our family is glad to see her. We hope she likes our home.

Soon it is time to eat. We use our best dishes for the food. We take out the best glasses. Then we sit down and eat together. Grandmother smiles and smiles.

I like this food! The cake is good, too!

We want to make Grandmother glad that she came to see us. So we think of special things to do for her. In Japan, Grandmother does not bake cakes. So I make her one.

My mother makes crab rolls for Grandmother.

Long Vowels: *ai, ay; ee, ea; oa, ow* and Compound Words

On the River

It's the end of the day.

> Well, we don't have any fish.

> No, but we had a neat day, and it didn't rain!

Look Back at *On the River*

CHECK YOUR UNDERSTANDING

1. Why does Shane's granddad take him to the river?

2. What kinds of animals do Shane and his granddad see?

3. Do you think Shane has a good time on the river? Tell why or why not.

WORD WORK: Long e

Find all the words in the story with the long e sound. Circle them. Then write each word on an index card. Put all the words spelled with *ee* in one group. Put all the words spelled with *ea* in another group. Read the cards aloud to a partner.

weekend   eat

Unit 7   Pack Your Bags!

In late June, Shane always spends a weekend with his granddad. This year Granddad takes him to Greenstone River. It's a good place to fish. You can also see a lot of wildlife there.

Is that rain?

I don't think so.

It's almost sunset. Still no fish. Shane asks if fish like this spot.

Fish like deep water. Once I caught a trout this big here.

They wait for the fish to bite. While they wait, Shane sees something.

Look!

That's a bald eagle! It hunts for small animals that live by the water. It eats fish, too.

Shane hears something in the cattail plants.

Look at the toad!

That's a tree frog. Frogs can be hard to spot. They sleep in the daytime.

© Hampton-Brown

4

5

Look Back at About Duke

CHECK YOUR UNDERSTANDING

1. Who is Duke?

2. Why does Chen miss him?

3. How do you think Chen felt after he talked to Duke? What will Chen do next?

WORD WORK: Verb Ending -ed

Circle all the verbs that end with -ed. Underline the root words. Then read each word to a partner. How many different sounds for -ed does your partner hear?

Verbs That End with -ed

wai̲t̲ed̲	lik̲ed̲
jog̲ged̲	hun̲t̲ed̲

Celebrate the Past

Children are singing as we leave the fair. I look back, wondering if we really went into the past.

It's fun to celebrate the past this way!

© Hampton-Brown

Look Back at Celebrate the Past

CHECK YOUR UNDERSTANDING

Make a concept map to tell about the Old English Fair.

- Old English Fair
  - Food
  - Things to Do
    - dress up in costumes

WORD WORK: Verb Ending -ing

Circle the verbs in the story that end in -ing. Write the words in a chart.

Add -ing	Drop silent e and add -ing	Double the consonant and add -ing
dressing	taking	scrubbing

People are dressing in costumes. We want to dress up, too. Sam has a velvet cap. Todd is pinning a ribbon on another hat.

Will this look good with braids?

Let's put on these hats.

We are eating very odd food today. Todd is tasting something called "toad in the hole." I am feasting on "beef on a stick."

I am getting hungry!

Do you need a bite to eat?

They are playing tunes just like people played 400 years ago! A young man is twirling sticks.

Some women are scrubbing clothes in a stream. They are joking and slapping the cloth on rocks.

I like the way they talk.

I do, too. They speak the way people spoke long ago.

RESCUE at the BEACH

Thanks! You tried to warn me. You are a great lifeguard!

Look Back at Rescue at the Beach

CHECK YOUR UNDERSTANDING

1. Why does Ann get into trouble?

2. How does Deb rescue Ann?

3. What do you think Ann will do the next time she tries surfing?

WORD WORK: Long Vowels

Circle all the words in the story with the long *i* sound. Underline all the words in the story with the long *u* sound.

Write the words in the chart. Write each word one time.

ie	igh	ui	ue
skies	bright	suit	blue

The skies are blue and the water feels great.
Ann and Kim plan to have a good day at the
beach. They meet Deb on the sand.

Hi, Deb. I like
your bright
red suit.

Thanks, Ann! It's
my lifeguard suit.

This time, Ann listens. She does
what Deb tells her.
Deb meets Ann and helps her to
the shore.

You gave me a
fright! I'm glad
you are safe.

Ann is surprised that Deb is a lifeguard. Kim isn't.

It's true that Deb is small, but she is a really strong swimmer.

I hope she never needs to rescue me.

Ann tries to fight the wave. Another high wave is coming. Deb yells to Ann. She tells Ann what to do.

Don't fight the wave! Let the next wave bring you in!

DANGER KEEP AWAY FROM ROCKS

LIFEGUARD

Ann is in a rush to get in the water and start surfing. She is between the waves and the rocks. She doesn't see the sign about the rocks. Deb tells her to watch out.

Ann doesn't listen to Deb. Then a big wave takes her close to the rocks. She needs help! Deb runs as fast as she can.

Community Bulletin Board

Car Wash

Start the Year Right!

Be an Artist for the Day

Art in the Park

March 31

Teens Reach Out and Recycle

We need things for our yard sale NOW! Chairs, tools, games, skirts, shirts, French horns! Don't throw them away. We can use them! Call 555-9146.

Look Back at Community Bulletin Board

CHECK YOUR UNDERSTANDING

1. Which group helps animals?

2. Which happens first, the concert or the car wash?

3. Which way of helping sounds good to you? Tell why.

WORD WORK: R-Controlled Vowels

Work in a group of three. Choose one of these words: *star, year, chair.* Work with your partners to think of words that rhyme with your word. Write the words on index cards.

star

year

chair

All around the world, teens use their time and skills to help others. Teens in this country are no different. American teens use their skills to make the world a better place. Look around your city for a community bulletin board like the one on these pages. Find your own way to make a difference!

Start the Year Right!

Come and hear how to protect birds. Join **The Bird Group**. Sundays at 2:00 p.m., on the porch of The Country House, 524 Third Street (near Hassan's Market).

Chirp!

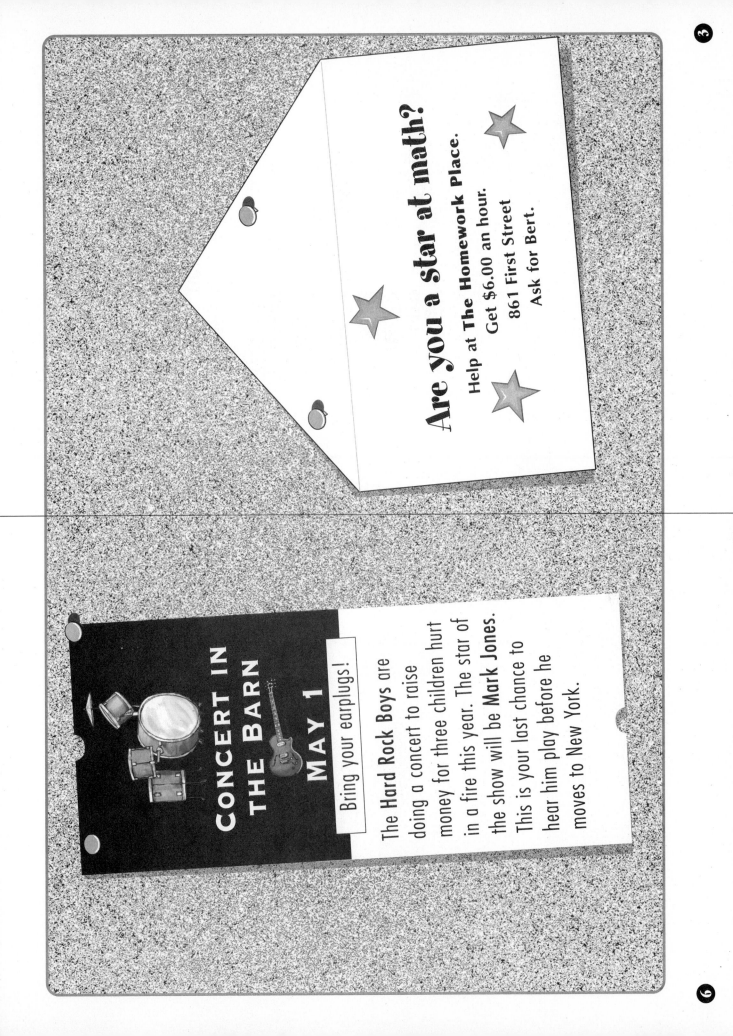

Are you a star at math?

Help at **The Homework Place**.

Get $6.00 an hour.

861 First Street

Ask for Bert.

CONCERT IN THE BARN

MAY 1

Bring your earplugs!

The **Hard Rock Boys** are doing a concert to raise money for three children hurt in a fire this year. The star of the show will be **Mark Jones**. This is your last chance to hear him play before he moves to New York.

Car Wash
$5.00
We get the dirt off!

Help our school band take a trip to Bear Mountain.

Bring your car to Park School, 10 Park Drive, on March 30.

(Go north on Fern Lane. Turn right on Park Drive. Park at the curb.)

Be an Artist for the Day

Make Art in the Park

March 31

You can paint. You can weave or make a clay pot. Funds will be used to add a room to Deerfield Senior Center.

The Perfect Moose

The perfect moose may live for as long as 12 years.

Look Back at *The Perfect Moose*

CHECK YOUR UNDERSTANDING

1. Where do moose live?

2. What happens to the male moose in the winter and spring?

3. Look back at the article. Pick one interesting fact you learned. Share it with a partner.

WORD WORK: R-Controlled Syllables

Work with a partner. Find words with these syllables.

per	ber	mer
for	ter	der

Both of you write each word on an index card. Take turns reading the words aloud. Hold up the word your partner reads.

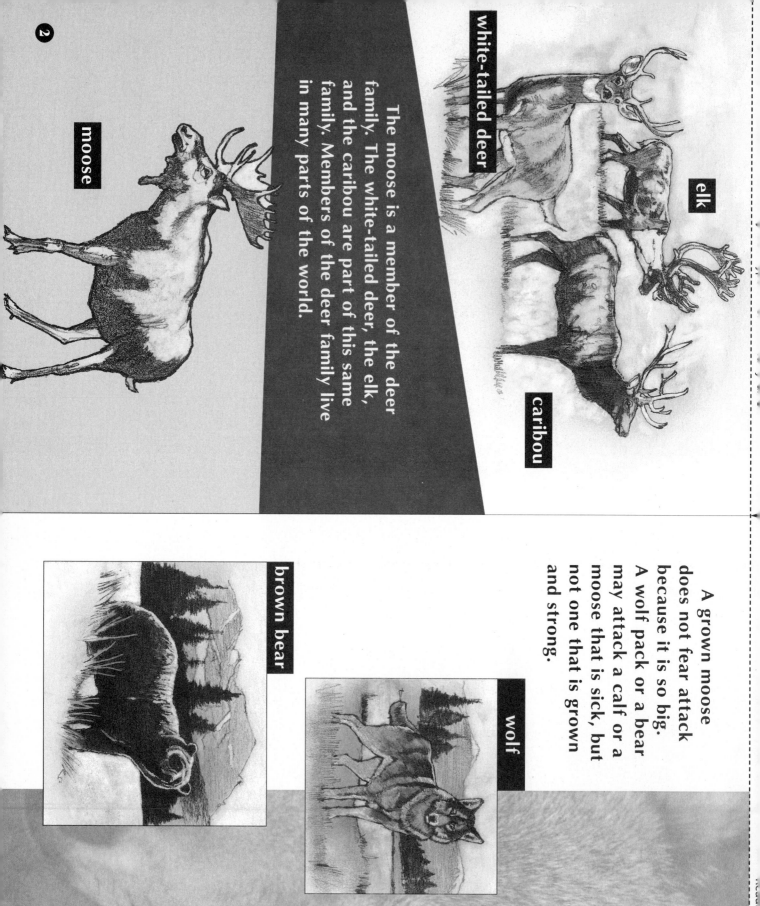

white-tailed deer

elk

caribou

The moose is a member of the deer family. The white-tailed deer, the elk, and the caribou are part of this same family. Members of the deer family live in many parts of the world.

moose

A grown moose does not fear attack because it is so big. A wolf pack or a bear may attack a calf or a moose that is sick, but not one that is grown and strong.

wolf

brown bear

Moose live in northern mountains and forests. A mother is called a cow. A baby is called a calf. Calves are born in the spring and stay with the mother for a year. Then the mother chases them away, and they must survive on their own.

calf cow

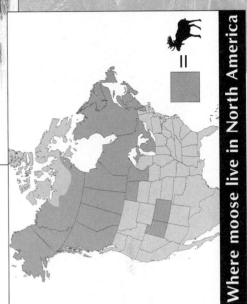

Where moose live in North America

=

Moose like water and are expert swimmers. They wade in ponds and lakes to eat the plants that grow under the water. They also eat twigs and shrubs on land. Moose will not hunt animals, but some animals hunt them.

© Hampton-Brown

Moose like to live alone. They do not form herds like other members of the deer family. When there is a lot to eat, three or four moose may stay together for a while.

The male, or bull, has big antlers. He uses the antlers to fight other bulls during mating time. Bulls shed the antlers in the winter and grow new antlers in the spring.

hump

bell

antlers

Kathy's Diary

Look Back at *Kathy's Diary*

CHECK YOUR UNDERSTANDING

1. How does Kathy feel in the first diary entry? How does she feel in her last entry?

2. What did people do on the day the war ended?

3. Do you think Kathy's diary is interesting? Tell why or why not.

WORD WORK: Words with y

Make a list of all the words in the story that end in y. Write each word in a chart one time.

y sounds like the long i in	y sounds like the long e in
sky	study

Unit 13 | Past and Present

Back in 1945, Kathy Grady started a diary. She wrote about her life during that time.

Each page Kathy wrote is called an entry. Here are some entries from Kathy's diary.

In 1960, Kathy is all grown up. She has two children of her own. She reads her diary to them. Her kids like to hear about life in the 1940s. It seems like a long time ago, but the words in Kathy's diary bring the past to life.

Daddy went to Italy three years ago. He is in the Army Air Force. He flies a big plane called a B-42.

This picture shows my dad with some of his buddies. Dad is the second man on the right. We miss him so much!

My dad is home!

One of his Army buddies is with him. We feel so lucky to have him back! Mom is happier than ever. She is going to make french fries and hamburgers. They are Dad's favorite foods.

Some nights we sit and study the sky. We are watching for our boys to fly home. Many of them have been away for four years!

People say the war may end soon! We all wait for that happy day.

The war is over! People are yelling and waving flags. You can hear their cries of joy. We all act silly. Mom is playing music and dancing.

I rushed out to get a newspaper. Dad can read it when he gets home.

A Pinch of Salt

The neighbors clapped with joy. At last, they all sat down to eat. They chatted and joked and ate lots of stew, just as they always did.

Enjoy!

Mmmm! Great stew!

The best ever!

Look Back at *A Pinch of Salt*

CHECK YOUR UNDERSTANDING

1. How does the woman make the stew?

2. What do the neighbors add to the stew?

3. The story says the woman was wise. Do you agree? Why or why not?

WORD WORK: Diphthongs and Variant Vowels

Say the name of each picture.

Find words in the story with the same vowel sound. Write them on cards. Compare the cards. How many ways is the vowel sound spelled?

Once there was a wise woman named Mrs. Paul. She lived in a small house at the end of town. She was not rich, but all her neighbors loved her. One morning the woman saw that her cupboard was empty. She found only a few peas to eat. She was too proud to beg, but she was too smart to stay hungry.

She put the peas into the pot. She filled the pot with water. Then she put the pot over the fire, just as she always did.

It was time for the woman to add one last thing, just as she always did. She added a pinch of salt. She stirred the pot, then tasted the stew again.

Perfect!

When the pot began
to simmer and steam, she
called to her neighbors.

Join me for a
pot of stew!

We will
join you!

Thank you!

All the neighbors heard her call.
They nodded and smiled, just as they
always did.

The woman tasted
the stew. She frowned.

This stew
tastes awful!

The neighbors smiled and
waited, just as they always did.

Soon, a crowd of neighbors entered her house. They each added food to the pot. They added carrots, meat, onions, and more peas. They filled the pot to the brim, just as they always did.

The pot boiled over the fire. By noon, the smell of rich stew filled the small house. It made the neighbors hungry.

Variant Vowels and Consonants

A Good Game

Mel

Gene

Rick

Can't I just hit the puck from here?

Sure!

He skates, and he falls. He falls, and he skates. He falls twice in a row, but he's such a good sport. Gene's friends knew he would have fun at hockey!

Look Back at A Good Game

CHECK YOUR UNDERSTANDING

1. Why do Mel and Rick take Gene to the ice rink?

2. How does Gene show he is a good sport?

3. Do you think Mel and Rick are good friends to Gene? Tell why or why not.

WORD WORK: Words with c or g

Work with a partner. Circle all the words in the story that have the letter g. Have your partner circle all the words in the story with the letter c. Write your words on index cards. See how many words your partner can read in 7 seconds. Then it's your turn to try.

good

Gene's friends take him to the ice rink to play hockey. There are kids on the ice already. They are playing a game. This is Gene's first time on skates.

Gene looks at the other kids. They are moving so fast! At last, Gene gets on the ice. He puts one foot in front of the other. He's on his feet, and he's skating!

Gene sits at the edge of the ice. While he puts on his skates, he watches the players on the ice. Some of them are huge!

Look how fast they're going!

Tie the laces tight.

Mel wants to be sure Gene is safe.

The boys are ready to play. Mel shows Gene the puck. Rick gives him the wooden stick.
    Gene does not think he will be good at hockey.

Try to knock the puck into the cage.

I can't even stand up!

You're going to love this game, Gene.

POSTCARDS from DEVEN

Southwestern States

Arizona New Mexico

Last night we camped under a million stars! A coyote howled at the moon. Dad told funny stories about cowboys in the desert. I think we laughed for hours. I want to come back here soon.

See you next week. I have a lot of pictures to show you.

Look Back at *Postcards from Deven*

CHECK YOUR UNDERSTANDING

1. Name three of the places Deven went. Tell what he saw at each place.

2. Tell about Deven's night in the desert.

3. What type of things did Deven do on his vacation?

WORD WORK: Multisyllabic Words

canyon	explore	hundreds
awake	around	cabin
music	even	until

Copy each word on one side of a card. On the back write its syllables. Show the card to a partner. Have your partner blend the syllables and tell you the word.

Hey, Brent! I am at Four Corners. This is the place where four states share a border. It is the only place in the U.S. like this. I stood on all four states at one time! Dad took a great picture of me.

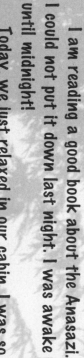

Cabin near Flagstaff, Arizona

I am reading a good book about the Anasazi. I could not put it down last night. I was awake until midnight!

Today, we just relaxed in our cabin. I was so tired. Dad got us big burritos for lunch.

There's a country-western music show later. I am going to dance and dance!

EXPLORE AMAZING UTAH!

Today, we went hiking in the mountains near Four Corners. It was hot in the valley below. We walked for three hours to get to the top. It's so high up there! You can see for miles! It was much cooler, too. We even had to wear our jackets.

White Water Rafting in Arizona

This is the most amazing place on Earth! We went rafting on the river. The red and brown canyon walls around us are taller than my house. The river took us over fast rapids. The water was very cold. It felt great in the hot sun.

Arches National Monument,
Utah

Wow! This place is great. There
are thousands of big red rocks here.
Some look like skyscrapers and
bridges, too. You need to see them
sometime. I didn't want to leave.

Mesa Verde, Colorado

Today, we got to explore some cliff dwellings.
The Anasazi people built them hundreds of years
ago. There are many rooms in the cliffs. In fact,
the rooms form a village. There are ladders that
go into some of the rooms. Some rooms have
round towers.

Prefixes and Suffixes

The Orchard

Late at night, I go outside and think about my great-grandfather. I'm so happy to share the gift he left my family so long ago.

Look Back at *The Orchard*

CHECK YOUR UNDERSTANDING

1. What gift did the great-grandfather give to his family?

2. Tell the different ways the family enjoys this gift.

3. Think of a gift a family member gave you. How is it like Great-grandfather's gift? How is it different?

WORD WORK: Prefixes and Suffixes

Find the words in the story that mean:

> not ripe
> use again
> without end
> not like
> full of harm
> in a careful way

Write the words and read them to a partner.

My family has a beautiful peach orchard. My great-grandfather planted the trees as a special gift to his family. Every summer, we all gather to pick the plump fruit from the trees. We are very thankful for the trees.

We boil the filled jars. This kills any harmful bacteria in the fruit. After the jars cool, we label each one.

Our canned fruit is unlike anything you buy in a store. Sometimes when we give a jar away, the people bring back the empty jar and ask for a refill!

Dad gently washes each peach. I peel the skin and remove the pits. Mom carefully packs the fruit into the jars and covers it with cupfuls of warm, sticky syrup. Then we screw on each lid tightly.

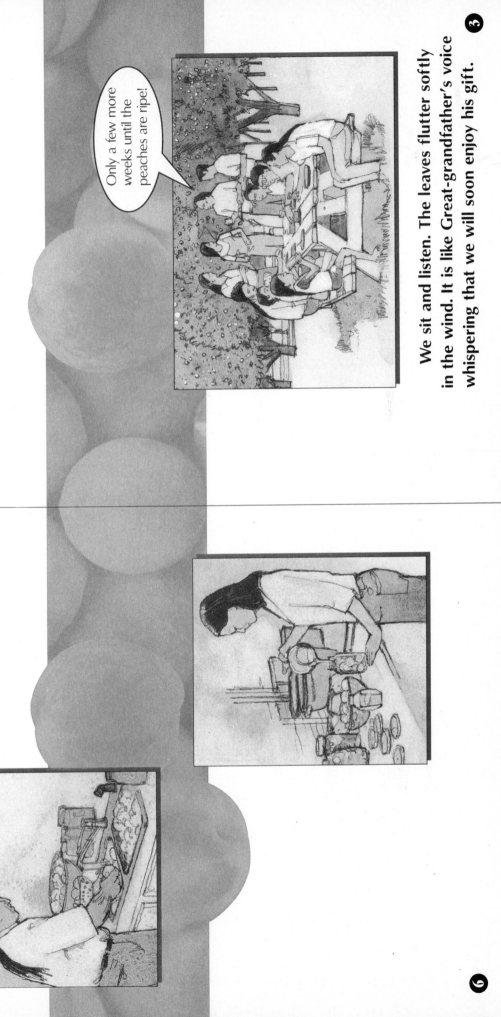

We wait all year for the peaches to grow. In the late winter, small pink buds appear on the trees. The flowers blossom. Then the petals fall off and float silently to the ground. In the spring, the fuzzy peaches start to form. We set up a big picnic table near the branches full of hard, unripe fruit. We all eat together under the shade of the trees.

We sit and listen. The leaves flutter softly in the wind. It is like Great-grandfather's voice whispering that we will soon enjoy his gift.

When summer is finally here, there is endless work outdoors. All of the family and countless friends arrive. Everyone is so helpful. We carry crates and pick the healthy fruit.

We have a lot of fresh peaches, so we put some in jars to enjoy in the winter.

When it's time to can the fruit, there is endless work indoors. We unpack boxes of glass jars that we reuse from year to year. We still have a few jars from when Great-grandmother canned peaches years ago!

Meteor Shower

The Geminids will come again next year, too. Look for them. If the sky is clear, you will be amazed, too!

Look Back at Meteor Shower

CHECK YOUR UNDERSTANDING

1. What is a meteor?

2. Why does the boy take his friends to the top of a hill on December 13?

3. Why will they always remember this night?

WORD WORK: Multisyllabic Words

Find 5 words with two syllables. Write each word on a strip of paper. Cut each word into syllables. Scramble the strips of paper. Then ask a partner to match the syllables and read the word aloud.

mid	dle
sea	son

It's the middle of the night on December 13. It is winter, the darkest season of the year. My friends wonder what I am going to show them. They grumble as we trudge up the steep hill.

It's too cold!

It's so dark!

What are we looking for?

What a fantastic way to celebrate the darkest season of the year! My friends and I will always remember this night.

I smile and lead them up the hill. I did not tell them what is going to happen. I want them to be surprised. I know they will enjoy the show. I check my watch. It's eleven p.m. The night sky will soon be filled with hundreds of shooting stars, or meteors, whizzing past the earth. I can hardly wait.

Look! Look!

Suddenly hundreds of meteors begin to shoot across the sky. It's like a fireworks display! My friends do not grumble anymore. They are really glad they came. We huddle beneath blankets and watch the amazing show.

Meteors are bits of space dirt. They hurtle through space at great speeds. Some pass very close to Earth. They burn up in the layer of gas that surrounds the planet. Meteors look like bright balls of fire as they burn. Most burn out and then fall to the earth as dust.

Sometimes a meteor does not burn up and crashes into Earth with a great bang! That does not happen very often.

The meteor shower begins right on time. My friends are excited to see the first shooting star. I do not tell them that there will be more—many more.

Look! A shooting star!

Yes! There's another one! Where do they come from?

These meteors are called Geminids because they appear to come from a group of stars called Gemini. I look in the sky for that group of stars. I tell my friends that Gemini means "The Twins" in Latin. I point to The Twins in the night sky.